Creative Copies

This exhibition and book are made possible
by a generous grant from Unisys
Corporation.

UNiSYS

British Airways is the official airline of The
Drawing Center.

The Drawing Center gratefully
acknowledges public funds from the New
York State Council on the Arts and the
Institute of Museum Services.

Creative Copies

Interpretative Drawings
from Michelangelo to Picasso

Egbert Haverkamp-Begemann
with Carolyn Logan

The Drawing Center
A nonprofit space for the study and exhibition of drawings,
New York

9 April–23 July 1988

Designed by Roy Cole
Typeset and printed by BAS Printers Limited,
Over Wallop, Hants
Bound by Hunter and Foulis Limited, Edinburgh

Contents

Foreword

Since its opening in January 1977, The Drawing Center, a nonprofit institution, has sought, through exhibitions and educational events to express the diversity, quality and importance of drawing – the creation of unique works on paper – as a major art form. Each year the Center presents five exhibitions. Those of an historical nature complement the Center's *Selections* series – group exhibitions of drawings by promising artists whose work is shown by the Center for the first time in New York. These are chosen from the Center's ongoing Viewing Program. Through this program, over 2500 artists each year are able to make appointments to show their drawings to curators, or leave a portfolio for viewing by the curatorial staff. In each of the four annual exhibitions, the work of eight to fifteen artists is shown. In the past eleven years, over 400 artists have been seen in forty *Selections* exhibitions. Eighty-five of these artists are now in the collections of museums around the world including the Albertina. These exhibitions are very special to the Center since every well known artist – even Michelangelo or Picasso – was at one time promising and unknown.

Creative Copies is a great event for The Drawing Center. The book wonderfully complements our other exhibition catalogues. Our first historical catalogue was *The Drawings of Antonio Gaudi* written by the distinguished architectural historian George R. Collins who was also the author of *Visionary Drawing of Architecture and Planning*. Vincent Scully was the author of *The Travel Sketches of Louis I. Kahn*. John Harris was the author of *Great Drawings from the Royal Institute of British Architects*. Other landmark exhibitions and catalogues for us have been *Sculptors' Drawings Over Six Centuries* with Colin Eisler as author; *Reading Drawings: A Selection from the Victoria and Albert Museum* with Susan Lambert as author; *Drawings from Venice: Masterworks from the Museo Correr, Venice* with Terisio Pignatti and Giandomenico Romanelli as authors. Last year we published *The Art of Drawing in France 1400–1900: Master Drawings from the Nationalmuseum in Stockholm* by Per Bjurström.

The theme of this exhibition and book has intrigued Egbert Haverkamp-Begemann for a long time. He has been working on the project for over three years together with the students and staff of The Drawing Center. I am proud to say their research has revealed extraordinary insights into the meaning of some very famous drawings such as Rembrandt's *The Last Supper* after Leonardo in the Lehman Collection at the Metropolitan Museum of Art. Their findings have clarified the inspiration and creative workings of some 44 artists over five centuries.

Professor Begemann is an important friend to The Drawing Center. He helped plan our new space and, unfailingly, his advice is not only brilliant but also very human and kind. He is on the Advisory Board of The Drawing Center.

Other members of the Advisory Board whom I would like to thank are Per Bjurström, Director of the Nationalmuseum of Stockholm; Dennis Farr, Director of the Courtauld Galleries; John Harris, formerly Keeper of the Royal Institute of British Architects; C. Michael Kauffmann, Director of the Courtauld Institute; Giandomenico Romanelli, Director of the Civic Museums of Venice and Pierre Rosenberg, Conservateur en Chef, Louvre.

More than anyone else, I would like to thank Mrs Felix G. Rohatyn. Singlehandedly she has made it possible for us to present this exhibition and to move into our new home. All of us who are involved with The Drawing Center applaud her courage, resourcefulness, and perseverance. She has lent The Drawing Center and its projects a certain magic. I am very grateful. Very special thanks go to Mrs Walter N. Thayer, Vice-Chairman of the Board. Day-to-day gratitude goes to all the directors of The Drawing Center for their constant support: James M. Clark, Jr.; Mrs Colin Draper; Colin Eisler; Michael Iovenko; Werner H. Kramarsky; William S. Lieberman; Mrs Gregor W. Medinger; and Edward H. Tuck. Special thanks go to my colleagues, Elinore Antell, Director of Development; Peter Gilmore, Exhibition Assistant and Janet Riker, Registrar/ Assistant Curator. Special thanks go to Joanne Maynard who typed the manuscript and whose enthusiasm has been infectious.

A personal note of thanks goes to Sir Colin Marshall, Paul Hopper, John Lampl, Frances L. Haak, and the many members of the cargo crew and flight personnel of British Airways who have handled the disparate demands of the shipping of very fragile drawings from all over the world and the travel of many couriers with skill, resourcefulness, unfailing courtesy and charm.

Finally, I would like to thank the following people who helped in innumerable ways: Mrs Vincent Astor, David Bancroft, John Barelli, Jacob Bean, Michael Beirut, Huntington T. Block, W. Michael Blumenthal, Kathryn Bonomi, Marc Perrin de Brichambaut, Margaret Holben Ellis, Linda Gillies, Bob P. Haboldt, Laura Hillyer, Anne Jackson, Heather Jones, Jeannette P. Lerman, John McGarrahan, Marceline McKee, Fraser D. Mooney, Richard Oldenburg, Andrew Oliver, James Pilgrim, Richard Pribnow, Felix G. Rohatyn, Robert Rosenblum, Patrick M. Talbot, Walter N. Thayer, Joline Tyhach, Lella and Massimo Vignelli, Alice Martin Whelihan, and Philip Wilson.

And last of all, thanks goes to Carolyn Logan for her scholarship and good spirits.

Martha Beck, Director

Acknowledgements

This exhibition owes its greatest debt to the owners who were willing to lend their drawings. Without the generosity of Her Majesty the Queen and many other lenders, and without the cooperation of their curators and staffs, this exhibition would not have been possible.

Martha Beck enthusiastically endorsed the idea of this exhibition as soon as it came to her attention. She realized it, solving the numerous and inevitable problems, with understanding and perseverance.

A special word of thanks is due to those Ph.D. students at the Institute of Fine Arts, New York University, who contributed to the study of the topic in a seminar under my supervision. They helped to select the drawings, and wrote entries for the catalogue. These entries were changed and edited, some of them barely, others substantially. They contributed excellent observations and analyses; ultimately I am responsible for errors and omissions.

Carolyn Logan, co-author of the introduction and contributor to the catalogue, assisted me in the review of the entries. Since many contributors were involved, her task was demanding. She completed it with cheerful intelligence. She also coordinated the comparative illustrations and saw to it that these became available for display in the exhibition and reproduction in the catalogue. Without her decisive help, this catalogue never would have been completed.

Some of the photography was carried out by Phil Evola, whose prompt and inventive helpfulness was much appreciated. Other faculty members, students, staff at the Institute of Fine Arts, too many to be mentioned, assisted in countless ways. Their contribution is gratefully acknowledged here.

Egbert Haverkamp-Begemann

List of Drawings and their Precursors

The Creative Copy

Interpretation, Imitation and Innovation

To copy and create seem contradictory concepts. Yet, throughout the centuries, artists were able to shape their own vision, however innovative or personal, only by absorbing the past. Artists have copied the works of their predecessors, imitated them, been stimulated by them, admired and criticized them. In their visual interpretation of both the real and spiritual world, artists were guided by the examples of the past and usually learned more from those examples than from reality itself. The copy, in its many manifestations, has played a fundamental role in the transmission and creation of ideas.

Copying is a vital part of imitation which, as is known to all educators, anthropologists, historians, is essential for didactic purposes; for the development of culture and thereby for the formation of the critical foundation for any personal action. We are aware of it in everyday life even more clearly than in art. A child develops its own individuality as a result of imitating his or her parents and other role models: every teacher knows that his or her example carries more weight than any other aspect of his instruction. In the twentieth century when the new and the different are at a premium in the arts, it may seem surprising that artistic models have played the same exemplary role.

The phenomenon of copying, marked by so many different aspects, almost all of them positive in the sense that they contribute to artistic formation and creativity, is served poorly by a word that is used largely in the derogatory sense of duplication. Certainly, copies as duplicates were made frequently, particularly before the advent of photography, usually by one artist or craftsman after work by another in order to produce a reproduction or second version. Duplication, however, does not concern us here.

A multiplicity of motives lies behind the act of copying works of art varying from artist to artist and from one copy or interpretation to another; usually each individual reaction to an older work of art represents a synthesis of the artist's intentions: to record; to interpret; to criticize and to learn. Each copy constitutes a dialogue between the interpreter and the interpreted; this dialogue fosters new solutions to problems shared by the two artists and creates new ideas. Since art not only belongs to the time in which it was made, but exists in subsequent time, an artist can learn from the generation that preceded him as well as from all previous generations of artists whose works have been preserved.

Drawing is the medium most appropriate for a dialogue with the past. Artists have interpreted art in all media, but drawing combines the qualities of immediacy and informality that other media lack: pen and ink or chalk are easily available and handle with rapidity, and are frequently used to satisfy the artist's needs rather than public expectation or demand. Prints after other works of art serve usually to propagate an image, paintings to duplicate, although in the nineteenth and twentieth centuries the oil sketch has evolved as a medium to freely interpret the past. Through the centuries, however, drawing has been the preferred medium when an artist wished either to record an image or to interpret it, to use it as a starting point for his own ideas or to criticize it. The artist's expectations and reactions reflected in such drawings are clearly discernible at this stage before their absorption into the artist's own style conceals their origin.

Drawings after other works of art illuminate the artist's link with the past as well as his ambition to change the future. These factors vary from one artist to the next, yet specific characteristics are discernible in each era. Similarities are also dependent on purposes that have remained the same throughout the centuries. Accuracy, verisimilitude and attention to detail have been aims of artists wishing to emphasize the characteristics of the work of art they copy in a seemingly objective way: submissively, without wishing to change the work substantially yet simultaneously deriving an impetus from it. Rubens (Cat. no. 19) and Goltzius (Cat. nos. 11, 12) admired classical sculpture; both made large, detailed renderings of some of the major classical monuments, adopting the sculptural language of classical antiquity as their own but with totally different effects. Their copying was motivated by admiration, as it was with Ingres when, in his youth, he learned from rendering classical busts (Cat. no. 50; see also p. 20) or later in life, when he realized his affinity to one of the greatest portraitists of equally noble elegance, Holbein (Cat. no. 51). Accurate copying can be largely documentary, yet can be carried out in the artist's own idiosyncratic, highly personal way, as Rubens and Ingres demonstrated in the drawings just mentioned and as Villon, Dufy, and Picasso confirmed in recent times (Cat. nos. 69, 70, 71). Rembrandt's transpositions of Mughal miniatures into his own medium and his own vocabulary (Cat. nos. 33, 34) represent extremes of maintaining the character of the original while transforming the artistic vehicle.

The selection of an example indicates the meeting of kindred spirits, the discovery by a later artist of a statement that is both familiar and stimulating. When Watteau copied Rubens (Cat. no. 38; see also p. 20), when Dürer copied Mantegna or selected motifs from Italian prints (Cat. nos. 3, 4; see also p. 17), or later when Degas recorded Uccello (Cat. no. 61), they did so because they recognized an effort to achieve what they wanted to achieve, were drawn to it and learned from it. Watteau, however personal his conception of feminine beauty, was much indebted to Rubens; Dürer to the Italian interpretation of the human body and Degas to previous representations of horse and rider.

This affinity aroused the artist's interest, he could quote from it or select details to enhance his own repertory of forms in order to learn from his predecessor's formulation of motifs or concepts. Frequently artists selected figures from other works of art to have a store of motifs: de Gheyn (Cat. no. 15); Rubens (Cat. nos. 16, 17); Delacroix (Cat. nos. 56, 59); Degas (Cat. no. 60), thereby adhering to the tradition of sample books (see also Boucher, Cat. no. 42). Sometimes such selections of figures, particularly with mature artists, simply became quotes of admired motifs (Rubens, Cat. no. 22).

Once enticed to react, the artist wished to take up a challenge. He sought to transform his model by expressing his own preferences and goals. Such transformations introduced in the course of absorbing the example graphically on paper, illuminate the later artist's intentions and concepts. Full of admiration for Masaccio's figures, Michelangelo endowed one of them with motion and volume essential to his view of art but alien to his predecessor's (Cat. no. 1), and Dürer, in a similar vein, infused a motif created by Maso Finiguerra with so much life and human feeling that the source is barely recognizable (Cat. no. 5). Rubens took figures from Michelangelo's *Brazen Serpent* and refashioned them to represent a subject that was only one motif in the fresco, in the process simplifying a complex biblical subject and teaching Michelangelo a lesson in the representation of contorted and foreshortened figures (Cat. no. 21). Rembrandt imposed his own concepts on the work he copied, most emphatically in his redefinition of Leonardo's *Last Supper* (Cat. no. 31). Here he contradicted the validity of more than one basic tenet of Leonardo's work. Specifically he declared the deep space to be injurious to the main subject of Christ and his disciples at the table, and opted for emphatic asymmetry to underscore the momentous drama of the event more effectively than Leonardo's timeless equilibrium.

The differences between the older work of art and its copy,

between the work of art and its reception, reveal some of the traits of those that react to the older work of art. When Tintoretto sketched Michelangelo's *Day* (Cat. no. 10) he preferred foreshortened views in keeping with his preference for figures that tumble and fly and that are so central to his work and when Claude copied Paul Bril (Cat. no. 29) he restructured the spatial relationship of foreground, middleground and view into the distance in a manner fully characteristic of his later work, while still revealing his source.

The purpose of these texts is to show the meeting of great artists and their interaction in the medium of drawing. They bring together some of the most telling and most beautiful examples that demonstrate the reaction and resulting action on the part of one artist in his encounter with the work of another. Such reactions and actions in copies, interpretations, quotes and variations, are all an integral part of the larger phenomenon of the reception and transformation of the artistic heritage by each successive generation. The study of such receptions and transformations is fundamental to the understanding of the art of each period.

History, Theory and Practice

Throughout the centuries, artistic theory, the admiration for classical antiquity, and academic precepts all have contributed, in one way or another, to the practice of copying. Young artists have always copied to train their hand and to become familiar with the artistic past, yet, copies have long been made by artists beyond their student years. As outlined in the previous essay, these copies are clearly motivated by the artists' admiration for the art of the past and their desire to learn from it, factors which transcend time. Nevertheless, the practice of copying also has parallels in artistic theories of imitation, theories which, over time, have been given different points of emphasis. This inquiry into the practice of copying in relation to the theory of imitation, is in no way definitive, but may illuminate the extent to which the copy is a product of its time.

With the formulation of new concepts concerning creative genius in the Renaissance, copying in the medium of drawing acquired increasing importance as an instrument to artistic representation. To elevate painting to the status of a liberal art, theorists beginning with Alberti in 1436, transferred the Aristotelian idea of imitation from the realm of poetry to that of painting. Art was to imitate nature as it ought to be. Hence, theorists and artists alike looked upon the art of antiquity as a means to sanction this theoretical viewpoint and as a model for the selection and combination of the most perfect parts of nature. Furthermore, to elevate the social stature of the artist, and subsequently to provide an institution for his training, the concept of the academy was appropriated and developed as an alternative to the apprenticeship system encouraged by the guilds.

In addition to receiving theoretical instruction in geometry, perspective, and proportion, the artist learned to master truth to nature initially by copying works of art. As early as *c.* 1390, Cennini wrote in his *Trattato della pittura*: 'Always take pains in drawing the best subjects which you can find, done by the hand of great masters . . . and it will happen that if nature has bestowed on you any invention, you will acquire a manner of your own, which cannot be other than good . . .' (Ch. 27). Cennini thus recognized the importance for the artist of copying from art, in order to imitate nature in his own manner.

Leonardo further developed this idea, prescribing a theoretical course of study in which the student was to learn by drawing – first after drawings, then after paintings, and finally after reliefs – before turning to nature. As Pevsner (1940) has shown, there is no evidence that Leonardo formed an academy, in the modern sense, in which to implement his theories. By 1490, however, Lorenzo the Magnificent took a first step in this direction, establishing a school for artists, among them the youthful Michelangelo, to study the ancient sculptures in his collection. Michelangelo also copied the frescoes of Giotto and Masaccio (Cat. no. 1), thus participating in the practice of copying that was to become the basis of all subsequent art education. These early pen and ink drawings bear the precisely delineated cross-hatchings which Michelangelo learned from Ghirlandaio, yet his figures deviate from their example. As Cennini said, the aim of copying the work of great masters was not only to learn from the past but to stimulate the development of innate artistic gifts. Even in his student work, Michelangelo's genius is apparent.

Artists north of the Alps followed the Italian model. As Meder (1923) and others have discussed, Dürer instructed the apprentice to copy the work of good craftsmen in order to develop a free hand of his own. The early and careful copies he made around 1494 after Italian prints (Cat. nos. 3, 4) – the vehicle by which he gained a knowledge of classical antiquity – already are inventive variations on their models. Dürer believed copying to be only a preliminary step towards representing nature in a creative yet informed manner, for a good painter was to be 'inwardly full of figures', or ideas. Dürer's later work illustrates how copying stimulates invention, for many of the Italian figures he copied reappear in a northern guise.

In the sixteenth century, the age of *maniera*, the imitation of styles and the quotation of forms from the work of previous masters gradually superseded the imitation of nature as a means for artists to attain an ideal in art. Vasari wrote in his *Vite* (1550, 1568): 'Our art is all imitation, of nature for the most part, and then, because man cannot by himself rise so high, of the works executed by those whom he judges to be better than himself'. Thus he called upon artists to synthesize aspects of antique and Renaissance works with the study of nature to conform to their ideas of absolute beauty.

As a result, the practice of copying in the medium of drawing took on a new dimension, becoming not just a means to an end but an end in itself. While the young artist copied to train his hand – as in the fifteenth century – the mature artist copied also, in the sense that he appropriated forms and styles, which he then combined in an original manner. In drawing, this recomposition of motifs borrowed from diverse sources was rarely achieved as it was in painting, nevertheless, the process of borrowing itself is often apparent. Schiavone appropriated the style of Parmigianino when, in the 1530s, he copied a print from Raphael's *Assembly of the Gods* (Cat. no. 9), to explore an alternative rendering of the narrative in which the protagonist takes centre stage. So too, at the same time in the north, did Jan Swart appropriate forms from Dürer (Cat. no. 6) which he incorporated without modification into his own settings when making designs for stained glass. Artists exploited the possibilities for invention and variation inherent in *maniera*. But so constrained a theory of imitation made the practice of faithful copying a most fundamental element of artistic representation.

During the seventeenth century, in reaction against the slavish imitation of *maniera*, theorists advocated more inventive forms of imitation. They did not discourage the artist from copying at the early stage of his career (indeed, academies arose in burgeoning numbers and propagated the practice of copying for didactic purposes), nor from borrowing creatively at later stages, but, in general, they did call upon artists to attain a mastery of their own style.

This theoretical bias was evident as early as 1604 when Karel van Mander published his didactic poem in which he wrote, when dwelling on imitation: 'well cooked turnips make good soup'. Making a pun on 'rapen', Dutch for 'turnip' as well as for 'to gather together', he thus argued for selective or critical use of past examples and against slavish copying. Ultimately derived from classical rhetoric, such theory was known and applied in the Renaissance, particularly by literary critics. No artist before Rubens, however, practised this theory as conscientiously as he did in his work as a copyist. The first northerner to fully synthesize the Italian artistic vocabulary into his own native one, Rubens was guided by his humanistic sensibility and creative genius not just to record, but to interpret and make judicious use of the ancient and Renaissance works he encountered, particularly when in Italy between 1600 and 1608. As Muller (1982) has shown and stated eloquently: 'His copies, adaptations, and transformations of earlier art implement the process of choice, judgement, and synthesis outlined by Quintilian and Seneca'.

Van Hoogstraeten, writing in 1678, however, criticized Rubens for his borrowing. Following an earlier suggestion made in the same vein by Philip Angel in 1642, he pleaded: 'With all your might, oh, you industrious youth of painters, try to train yourself to become able in your own inventions'. As a former pupil of Rembrandt, he thereby professed what his teacher had practised. When Rembrandt reworked a model, the result sometimes was as much an invention of his own as a copy of another artist's work as in his redefinition of Leonardo's *Last Supper* (Cat. no. 31). His work in general, so thoroughly incorporated the art of Italy as well as of other cultures, whether German or Mughal (Cat. nos. 33, 34), that their fundamental importance, as catalysts rather than examples, becomes apparent only with close study.

In Italy, Bellori called upon the artist to utilize his inventive faculties, much as van Hoogstraeten did, but with a marked shift in emphasis. In his view, the proper object of artistic imitation was the Idea, or the artist's inner vision of ideal beauty. As he phrased it in his essay of 1664, *L'Idea dei pittore*: 'The Idea, originating in nature, supersedes its origin and becomes the origin of art'. Bellori's notion that this Idea be formulated by a process of selection from nature constituted a return to the Aristotelian concept of imitation. This encouraged the practice of copying from the supreme representations, both ancient and modern, of idealized nature. Thus, as late in his career as the 1640s, Bellori's friend, Poussin, copied Raphael's *Parnassus* (Cat. no. 28), translating it with wash into a personal and expressive adaptation.

In France, the classicist theory of imitation formulated by Bellori was taken up and codified by the Academy. Established in 1648 by Colbert and Lebrun, the French Academy made education its primary purpose. The preliminary course of study consisted of drawing: from the drawings of masters, from plaster casts, and from life, paralleling Leonardo's programme. Moreover, the art of antiquity was copied by students and revered by all as a model of perfection. Even the 'querelle des anciens et des modernes', which called for a new naturalism in art in subsequent decades, did little to affect the role of copying; it only enlarged upon the models from which artists could draw. Thus in the eighteenth century, even though this classicist theory of imitation prevailed, Watteau and Fragonard turned to Rubens, and Boucher to Bloemaert (Cat. nos. 38–44), in addition to the traditional canon of Italian models, to learn from the past.

The development of the concept of original genius did little to undermine the theory of imitation. It merely came to be seen as a function of the artist's imagination. Thus into the nineteenth century, artists continued to draw from the past and in their best copies captured the spirit of the model as they interpreted it. Although strictly still a work of the previous century, Ingres' copy of 1793 from a cast after the antique (Cat. no. 50) betrays some of the noble simplicity and calm grandeur which Winckelmann so highly praised in Greek art. So too, did Delacroix, a half century later, find a linear equivalent in his copies (Cat. nos. 57, 58) for the energy and emotive power he so admired in Rubens's work.

In the twentieth century, despite the lack of any clearly defined theory of imitation, artists adapted the tradition of their predecessors to their own visions, copying to order to grapple with formal and expressive problems. Juan Gris, for example, copied the work of Cézanne (Cat. no. 68) to further explore the integration of figure and setting in a manner directly related to his experiments in Cubism. Picasso, however, copied not only to learn and experiment, but to consciously attach himself to historical tradition. By imposing his own vision and style in his recreations of works by his predecessors, he sought to surpass their example, as Rembrandt and others had before him.

Ever since the Renaissance, theoreticians have put forth their thoughts on how art should imitate and improve upon nature. All have acknowledged, with different points of emphasis, the role of past artistic examples and the importance of individual formulation and expression for the attainment of this goal. Over the centuries, artists, too, have shared these concerns and sought to learn from the past in order to render nature in their best, most personal and innovative manner. Less concerned by theory than theoreticians, artists often found their own solutions to imitating nature, as well as to reproducing their ideas on the physical and spiritual world, with the guidance of the example of admired predecessors. Their practice of copying thus has never been directly dependent on the theory of imitation but has always run a parallel course alongside it. Theories of imitation clarify certain aspects of copying in the course of time. Yet, copying always has been not only a stimulus to invention, but part of it and, as such, has a momentum of its own that can be neither restrained nor accelerated by theory.

E. H.-B
C.L.

Bibliographical Note

The best study of drawings after other works of art is still Joseph Meder's discussion of this subject in his book, *Die Handzeichnung, Ihre Technik und Entwicklung* (1st or 2nd ed., 1919; 1923, especially pages 251–276; preferable to the translation entitled *The Mastery of Drawing*, New York 1978, volume I, 217–231). Meder touched on all the main aspects of the subject but could not go into detail because of the comprehensive nature of this admirable book. Since then, there has been no comprehensive study, nor have drawings that copy or interpret art through the last four centuries been the subject of an exhibition.

Various aspects of the drawn copy (copy in the broad sense of the word), however, have received attention. The museum in Dresden staged an imaginative loan exhibition in 1970, which, paralleling in intention the one presented here, provided a strong incentive. It showed prints as well as drawings, and copies or interpretations as well as works influenced by specific examples, and thereby covered more ground (*'Dialogue' – Kopie, Variation und Metamorphose alter Kunst in Graphik und Zeichnung vom 15. Jahrhundert bis zur Gegenwart*, Kupferstichkabinett, by Werner Schmidt, Christian Dittrich, and others). Shortly before, in 1967, Matthias Winner and staff of the printroom in Berlin had organized an excellent exhibition at the museum in Dahlem, composed of drawings after classical sculptures and monuments from its own holdings. This exhibition, entitled *Zeichner sehen die Antike*, was accompanied by a scholarly catalogue. Drawings were included in the exhibition, *Art into Art* (1971), sponsored by the Burlington Magazine and held at Sotheby's in London. It dared to investigate and demonstrate the varied effects of specific works of art on works of later times in all media (by Benedict Nicolson, Keith Roberts, and others), while a section of the exhibition, *Drawing: Technique and Purpose*, at the Victoria and Albert Museum in 1981, and later shown at the Drawing Center accompanied by an enlarged catalogue, *Reading Drawings*, shared some ground with the topic of the present exhibition as well. One of the few studies on copying as a historical phenomenon in a restricted period of time was provided recently by H. Geissler, 'Die Zeichnungen des Augsburger Bildhauers Caspar Menellier', with the subtitle 'Überlegungen zum Kopierwesen in Deutschland um 1600', in the *Münchner Jahrbuch der bildenden Kunst* (3rd series, XXXIV, 1983, 59–100). The most stimulating and broad selection of drawings that have interpreted older works of art, however, was included by K. E. Maison in his well-designed book with short but penetrating commentary *Themes and Variations, Five Centuries of Master Copies and Interpretations* (London 1960; 2nd ed. 1966; in 1960 also published in Munich and Zürich under the title, *Bild und Abbild – Meisterwerke von Meistern kopiert und umgeschaffen*).

Apart from studies on individual printmakers and copies made by them, like that on Giulio Campagnola, or studies on artists as their work was disseminated in prints, such as that of Rubens, the reproductive print in the broad sense has been the subject of exhibitions: *Copies as Originals* in Princeton (1974, with some drawings); *The Inspired Copy* in Baltimore (1975), and *Bilder nach Bildern* in Münster (1976). Painted copies also have been the subject of exhibitions. The first one apparently was held in Mannheim in 1931 (*Schöpferische Kopien*, by G. F. Hartlaub; see also his 'Vom Sinn des Kopierens, zur Mannheimer Ausstellung "Schöpferische Kopien"', *Die Kunst für Alle*, XLVII, 1932, 157–161, 165–167), and Basel in 1937 for the opening of the Kunsthalle, which may have included drawings as well; the lecture given at the occasion by L. Lichtenhan was later printed in his *Beiträge zur Kunst* (Basel 1958, 15–19). The exhibition *Creative Copies*, at the Art Institute of Chicago in 1970, suggested by W. Stechow, may have included both paintings and drawings as well as prints (only a checklist survives), whereas the exhibition *Original – Kopie – Replik – Paraphrase* at the Akademie der bildenden Künste in Vienna, in keeping with the mission of the institution, was entirely devoted to painted copies, largely those made for education purposes (1980, with instructive essays by H. Hutter and others). The stimulating exhibition *Art about Art*, held at the Whitney Museum of American Art, New York, and elsewhere in 1978/79, dealt mainly with the reaction of Pop artists to past master works (by J. Lipmann and R. Marshall, with an illuminating essay by L. Steinberg). Refreshing, thought provoking, and sound, despite the general nature of the audience to which it was directed, was the issue 'Kunstenaars op Herhaling' of *Openbaar Kunstbezit* (XXIII, no. 4, 1979, 97–128 by J. de Vries, B. Broos, E. Meijer, and others).

Of vital significance for the study of the nature of copies, whether replicas or interpretations, is the examination of the spread and reception of classical sculpture. The publications, from E. Curtius and E. Ladendorf to M. Bieber, P. P. Bober, and B. S. Ridgway, cannot be enumerated here in spite of their significance. Although the literature of the theory of copying is sparse, that on the related concepts of imitation and mimesis is vast and widespread. Particularly useful, in general, but also specifically for the preparation of this catalogue and its essays, are the studies by E. Panofsky *Idea: Ein Beitrag zur Begriffsgeschichte der älteren Kunsttheorie* (Leipzig 1924; translated by J. J. S. Peake *Idea, A Concept in Art Theory*, New York 1968); A. Blunt *Artistic Theory in Italy 1450–1600* (Oxford 1940) and N. Pevsner *Academies of Art Past and Present* (Cambridge 1940). Mention should also be made of R. Wittkower's 'Imitation, Eclecticism, and Genius' (in *Aspects of the Eighteenth Century*, ed. by E. R. Wasserman, Baltimore 1965); the entry 'Mimesis', by Rosario Assunto and others, in the *Encyclopedia of World Art* (X, 1965, 93–122) and J. Muller's article, 'Rubens's Theory and Practice of the Imitation of Art' *Art Bulletin* (LXIV, 1982, 229–247). There are, needless to say, other useful publications like Donat de Chapeaurouge's *Wandel und Konstanz in der Bedeutung entlehnter Motive* (Weisbaden 1974) but the purpose here is not to give an extensive bibliography of the subject. The titles listed above all have been useful to the authors in one way or another.

This bibliographical note, however, should not be closed without paying tribute to a different comment on the nature of the artistic copy. Since the 1950s, contemporary artists have been reinterpreting the work of the past and using it for their own statements with increasing emphasis and intensity. One can think of Larry Rivers, Roy Lichtenstein, Sherry Levine, Mark Tansey, and others. Ultimately, their comments may well influence the art historian's view.

The Drawings

Editorial Note

Catalogue entries are arranged in approximate chronological order.

All drawings are on white or off-white paper unless otherwise noted.

Dimensions are given in millimetres; height precedes width.

References in the entries and notes are cited in full in the bibliography.

Catalogue entries are followed by the initials of the following contributors:

A.B.	Andrew Butterfield
J.C.	Judith Cohen
C.F.	Carina Fryklund
E.H.-B.	Egbert Haverkamp-Begemann
L.K.	Lisa Kurzner
C.L.	Carolyn Logan
C.M.	Christopher Miele
N.O.	Nadine Orenstein
P.V.	Paula Volent

Fig 1-1 Masaccio *Tribute Money*, (detail). Santa Maria della Carmine, Florence

Michelangelo Buonarroti

Caprese 1475–Rome 1564

1 St. Peter
From Masaccio's *Tribute Money*

Pen and brown ink (St. Peter) and red chalk (two studies of arms), tinted greyish blue around the principal figure by a later hand
315 × 197 mm
Verso: Various sketches and notations
Annotated at lower left, [*Mic*]*helAnge*; in lower right corner *39*[*?*]*8* with an indecipherable collector's mark
Bibliography: Frey 1909–11, no. 11; Wilde 1932, 47; Berenson 1938, 186 [*c.* 1492]; Tolnay 1943, 175–178 [1488]; Dussler 1959, 117–118 [*c.* 1495]; Weinberger 1967, 26–27; Hartt 1970, 27–28 [*c.* 1490]; Tolnay 1975, 25 (with further references) [early 1490s]; Wilde 1978, 19–25
Exhibitions: Florence 1964, no. 2; Munich 1967, no. 45

Munich, Staatliche Graphische Sammlung. Inv. no. 2191

As a youth, Michelangelo avidly studied and copied masterpieces of Florentine painting.[1] He was particularly attracted to Masaccio whose frescoes at the Carmine he is reported to have drawn for many months.[2] Of these studies, only one sheet undoubtedly after Masaccio survives – the drawing here exhibited of St. Peter from *Tribute Money* (Fig. 1–1).[3]

Michelangelo changed his model in a number of subtle but substantial ways. Masaccio's St. Peter stands with his weight on his back foot, holds his head down and in and sticks out his arm somewhat stiffly. The drapery is nearly symmetrical and reinforces the impression of gravity, balance and volume in the figure. In contrast, Michelangelo's Apostle steps forward and stretches his arm and hand before him, while his cloak, now vivid with light, registers the motions of different parts of his body.

It is revealing to examine some of the means by which Michelangelo effected this transformation. For instance, he elevated the Saint's hand and raised his index finger to make the gesture more pointed; enlarged the cuff to add force to the thrust of the arm; and copied the upper edge of the sleeve with a sequence of rapid, calligraphic lines that run from the back of Peter's robe to the end of his finger. Michelangelo also refashioned the fall of St. Peter's cloak. His major changes were to eliminate the deeply shaded fold along the front of Peter's garment and to give far greater emphasis to highlighted ridges of drapery. The visual difference this creates is that where Masaccio's figure seems to stop in a strong, stable vertical that serves as a strut for the arm, Michelangelo's figure ends with a fluid edge of kinetic energy that rises to the forward swing of Peter's gesture. In a similar manner, Michelangelo used chiaroscuro in the Apostle's upper body to show how the muscles of the back and neck are engaged by the movement of the Saint's head.

The emphasis on organic and articulate motion is a common trait in copies by the young Michelangelo. In his study from Giotto's Peruzzi Chapel (Fig. 1–2), for instance, the artist added a nearly serpentine twist to the pose of one of the figures.[4] In Giotto's fresco both the head and left hand of the standing figure are parallel to the picture plane. In the copy, Michelangelo tilted

1 St. Peter

Fig 1-2 Michelangelo Buonarroti *Copy after Two Figures from the Ascension of St. John the Evangelist by Giotto*. Musée du Louvre, Cabinet des Dessins, Paris

the man's head away from the viewer and placed his left hand, now strongly foreshortened, behind his head. The resulting tension is registered throughout the body, for example, in the sinewy neck, the right arm, and the changed position of the left foot.

Although students of Michelangelo generally agree on the order in which the artist made his early drawings, there is no consensus on what specific dates should be assigned to these works. The problem is that there are only two reference points at the start of his career as a draughtsman: 1488, when he is documented to have entered Ghirlandaio's studio, and 1490–92, when, on the basis of Vasari, he is believed to have copied in the Carmine. In the view of the present writer, we should also consider the *Battle of the Centaurs* as relevant comparative material. The figural style invested in this relief of 1490–92 is wholly consistent with the changes the artist made in his copy after Giotto.[5] On the grounds of technique, it is generally believed that this sheet must be earlier than the copy after Masaccio. Consequently, we can agree with Berenson and Tolnay that the latter drawing dates *c*. 1492.

Whatever the exact date of the drawing, Michelangelo constructed the figure with a technique of straight, parallel lines and dense cross-hatchings that he had learned from Ghirlandaio. He thus adopted his teacher's handling of the pen to revitalize a figure of another admired predecessor in a manner indicating the ambitions of a sculptor.[6]

A.B.

1   On this activity see, in particular, Berenson 1938, I, 185–187; Tolnay 1943, 176–179; Wilde 1978, 19–25.

2   Both Vasari/Milanesi 1568, 140 and Cellini/Symonds 1903, 20 testify to Michelangelo's copying in the Carmine for a long period.

3   Two drawings by Michelangelo in the Albertina, Vienna, inv. nos. S.R. 150r and S.R. 150v are almost universally recognized as Masacciesque in character and are believed to be copies from Masaccio's lost fresco, *La Sagra*, at the Carmine. Creighton Gilbert 1969, 260–277, however, argues convincingly that Michelangelo's drawing of a group of figures in Vienna, purportedly copied from Masaccio's lost *Sagra*, actually copies a lost drawing by Ghirlandaio after Masaccio's fresco.

4   Musée du Louvre, inv. no. 706r; see Tolnay 1975, 23–24.

5   One should compare specifically the head and neck of the standing figure in the drawing with those of the principal figure at the left in the relief.

6   Meder 1923, 36, 259–260.

Leonardo da Vinci

Vinci 1452–Amboise 1519

2 Moses
After Michelangelo's sculpture

Pen and brown ink; trimmed at top; laid down
100 × 94 mm
Provenance: Sir T. Lawrence (L. 2445); King William II of Holland
Bibliography: Venturi 1927, 59; Valentiner 1949, 343; Tolnay 1954, 150; Goldscheider 1959, 150; Maison 1966, 47, pl. 19; Clark and Pedretti 1968, I, 82, 113; Koevoets et al. 1976, 38, no. 28
Exhibitions: Amsterdam 1934, no. 570; Paris 1935 (I), no. 574; Los Angeles 1949, no. 82; Raleigh 1959, no. 28; Paris-Rotterdam-Haarlem 1962, no. 50; Amsterdam 1963, no. 91

Amsterdam, Amsterdams Historisch Museum, bequest C.J. Fodor. Inv. no. A-11020

This drawing was first identified by Valentiner as a copy of Michelangelo's *Moses* (Fig. 2–1).[1] Valentiner believed Leonardo drew it in 1515 at the time Buonarroti was at work on the sculpture for Julius II's tomb.[2] This identification of the drawing was subsequently accepted by both Tolnay and Clark and Pedretti.[3] The most recent publication of it,[4] however, has returned to A. Venturi's suggestion[5] that the drawing is a study for an Apostle in the *Last Supper*. Koevoets based this hypothesis on the drawing's similarity to another study in Vienna (Fig. 2–2)[6] that can be more clearly connected with Leonardo's painting.

While Koevoets's observation of the formal similarities of the nose, mouth and eyebrows of the men in the two drawings is certainly apt, he has overlooked evidence contrary to his opinion. To begin with, as Goldscheider, Valentiner and Clark and Pedretti have observed, on stylistic grounds the Leonardo in Amsterdam must be assigned a date which is considerably later than that of the sheet in Vienna.[7] Moreover, the similarities between the *Moses* and the Leonardo in Amsterdam are more numerous and fundamental than the similarities between the two drawings. For instance, like the *Moses*, the drawing here exhibited has a strong, square forehead, wind-swept hair, a long beard falling from the chin in two great locks and a right hand held against the upper chest. Even the form and expression of the man's face in the Fodor drawing are at least as similar to the *Moses* as they are to the Apostle in Vienna. If, as seems more probable, this sheet is a copy of the Michelangelo, then we must also note a series of striking differences between the drawing and the *Moses*. In the Leonardo, Moses is shown with covered, rather than bare, arms and there is a knot of drapery above his left shoulder. While in Michelangelo's sculpture Moses's head is pulled back and his right arm held down and close to his body, Leonardo depicts the prophet with his head straining forward and his right elbow raised. Finally, in the Leonardo drawing, Moses places his right hand immediately under his chin rather than near the middle of his chest.

A plausible explanation for these changes was given by Valentiner who believed the drawing to be a free sketch made from memory.[8] That Leonardo on another occasion changed the

David when he drew it from memory would seem to further the credence of this hypothesis.[9]

There is also the possibility that Leonardo drew not Michelangelo's final sculpture, but a model for the *Moses* instead. We are obliged to consider this proposition in the first regard because Leonardo cannot be documented in Rome in 1515 when Valentiner presumed the painter copied the statue.[10] Of greater consequence, studies Leonardo made in Milan between 1508–11 for the unbuilt Trivulzio Monument show Leonardo had intimate knowledge of the original plans of 1505 for the tomb of Julius II.[11] Finally, we know from the famous copy in Berlin of Michelangelo's drawing for the Julius tomb that at least as late as 1513, Moses was intended to have covered, rather than bare, arms.[12] As Leonardo is documented in Rome in 1513, it is possible he drew directly from a transitional model Michelangelo made at this time, one in which the *Moses* has evolved towards its final pose while still retaining the cloak originally intended.

Vasari wrote of Leonardo's *sdegno grandissimo* for Michelangelo.[13] His copying of unexecuted elements from the Julius tomb suggests Leonardo bore the greatest admiration rather than greatest disdain for the sculptor.

A.B.

1 Valentiner 1949.
2 Michelangelo was first commissioned to execute Julius II's tomb in 1505. In 1513, he signed a new contract with Julius's heirs and carved several statues for it including the *Moses*, which is generally believed to have been begun in 1515. The Julius tomb was not finished until it was erected in a much reduced form in S. Pietro in Vincoli between 1542–45. On the different projects for the tomb, see Tolnay 1954 and Pope-Hennessy 1985, 25–39, 311–324 and 452–453 with further references.
3 Tolnay 1954, 104; Clark and Pedretti 1968, I, 82, 113.
4 Koevoets et al. 1976, 38, no. 28.
5 Venturi 1927, 59.
6 Albertina, Vienna, inv. no. 17614; see Berenson 1938, fig. 502.
7 On the date of the drawing in Amsterdam, see Goldscheider 1959, 150 [c. 1514]; Valentiner 1949 [1515] and Clark and Pedretti 1968, I, 82, 113 [late].
8 Valentiner 1949.
9 Windsor Castle, Windsor, inv. no. 12,591r. According to Clark and Pedretti 1968, I, 117–118, this drawing was made in Milan c. 1507.
10 For a comprehensive list of documented dates in Leonardo's life, see Clark and Pedretti 1968, I, lix–lxi.
11 Clark 1952, 152; Clark and Pedretti 1968, I, 42–43. It is worth noting that Windsor 12,583A may also have been drawn for the Trivulzio Monument.
12 Tolnay 1954, 9–14, 33–34, pl. 96.
13 Vasari/Milanesi 1568, IV, 47.

2 Moses

Fig 2-1   Michelangelo Buonarroti *Moses*, (detail). San Pietro in Vincoli, Rome

Fig 2-2   Leonardo da Vinci *Half-figure of St. Peter*. Graphische Sammlung Albertina, Vienna

3 The Battle of the Sea Gods

Albrecht Dürer

Nuremberg 1471–1528

3   The Battle of the Sea Gods
From an engraving by Mantegna

Pen and brown ink
292 × 382 mm
Inscribed upper centre: *1494–AD*

Fig 3-1 Andrea Mantegna *Battle of the Sea Gods*, (right half).
Rijksprentenkabinet, Amsterdam

Provenance: Imperial Treasury; Imperial Library; Duke Albert
    Collection
Bibliography: Lippmann 1905, 455; Seidlitz 1907, 7; Tietze and
    Tietze-Conrat 1928, 63; Winkler 1936, I, 9, 60; Panofsky
    1948, I, 51 ff., 73; Maison 1966, 60, pl. 52; Koschatzky and
    Strobl 1972, no. 10 (with further references); Strauss 1974,
    no. 1494/13
Exhibitions: Paris 1950, no. 56; Nuremberg 1971, no. 511

Vienna, Graphische Sammlung Albertina. Inv. no. 3061, D. 34

The *Battle of the Sea Gods* is a subject Andrea Mantegna undoubtedly chose to engrave for the opportunity it afforded him to

Fig 3-2 Urs Graf after Mantegna *Battle of the Sea Gods*, Öffentliche Kunstsammlung, Kupferstichkabinett, Basel

represent the human figure engaged in a variety of actions, some-times strained and often violent, like Pollaiuolo had before him.[1] Mantegna took his cue from a classical relief, using two good-sized copperplates to accommodate its frieze-like width without having to sacrifice the size of the figures. These prints date from about the middle of the 1480s and by 1494 Dürer had access to at least one of them (Fig. 3–1). He copied it surely for the same reasons that had prompted Mantegna to make his prints in the first place.

In his drawing, Dürer carefully followed the print by first tracing the contours of the forms. Even so, he endowed them with a new vitality and when he came to fill in the details, he rethought the musculature and elaborated many particulars left vague by Mantegna.[2] The drawing shows us that already in 1494 Dürer was concerned with the structure of the human body. In the process of copying, he placed the horizon a little higher. This accords with his approach to landscape in his watercolour draw-ings of that period.[3]

Dürer's copy of Mantegna's *Battle of the Sea Gods* and a similar one after a second print by the same artist, the *Bacchanal with Silenus* both made in 1494, mark his first exposure to the art of the Italian Renaissance. Later that same year, in October, he left for a trip to Italy, returning to Nuremberg in May of 1495.[4] It is possible that his decision to journey south was stimulated at least in part by his acquaintance with these prints.

To the end of his life, Dürer sustained a deep interest in the work of Mantegna. A series of drawings, probably intended for woodcuts, which he embarked upon late in his career are directly dependent on Mantegna in narrative, composition, space, and even in the formulation of landscape.[5] Curiously, some of these Passion scenes of 1520/21 he designed while on a trip to The Netherlands. In 1528, the year of Dürer's death, the *Four Books of Human Proportion* were published. They represent the culmina-tion of Dürer's concentrated study of the human form which he had initiated three decades previously in studies such as this one after Mantegna.

Urs Graf also copied Mantegna's *Battle of the Sea Gods*, (Fig. 3–2). In contrast to Dürer, he took great liberties with Mantegna's design, eliminating the setting, changing some of the details, and minimizing the shading while adding a calligraphic touch to the linear contours of the figures. Graf must have been aware that Dürer later utilized the female figure with her arm raised on the left of Mantegna's print in reverse for his engraving of *The Combat of Virtue and Pleasure in the presence of Hercules* (B. 73). In his own copy after Mantegna's *Battle of the Sea Gods*, Urs Graf incorporated elements from Dürer's *The Combat of Virtue and Pleasure in the presence of Hercules* (Fig. 3–3), the horned head of the triton and the long stick brandished by the twisting figure in the background, but copied the female figure on the left as she appears in Mantegna's example.[6]

N.O.

1   The two engravings by Mantegna listed, described and illustrated by Hind 1948, V, 15, nos. 5 and 6, were discussed recently with successful new attempts at establishing their dates and answering a number of questions by Levinson, Oberhuber and Sheehan in Washington 1973, nos. 75 and 76.
2   A brief but perceptive analysis of Dürer's drawing (and the one after the *Bacchanal*, see below note 4) is given by Panofsky [1943] 1955, 31–32.
3   The first to observe the elevation of the horizon were Koschatzky and Strobl 1972, no. 10.
4   That Dürer made these copies before he left is supposed by Seidlitz, the Tietzes, Winkler, Koschatzky and Strobl. A certain lack of accomplish-ment in some details, emphasized by Winkler, seems to indicate an early date within the year of 1494.
5   Particularly Panofsky [1943] 1955, 218–220 stressed the Mantegnesque features of these drawings (Winkler 1939, IV, nos. 793–799).
6   Koegler 1926, no. 8 and Maison 1966, 60, pl. 51.

Fig 3-3 Albrecht Dürer *The Combat of Virtue and Pleasure in the presence of Hercules*

4 The Primum Mobile

Albrecht Dürer

Nuremberg 1471–1528

4 The Primum Mobile (The Prime Mover)
After an engraving by the Master of the Tarocchi

Pen and black ink with pale green and brownish red wash
190 × 106 mm
Bibliography: Tietze 1928, I, 14, no. 54; Winkler 1936, I,
no. 128; Hind 1938, I, 231; Panofsky 1948, II, no. 982 (with
further references); Strauss 1974, no. 1494/20
Exhibitions: London 1928, no. 189; London 1971 (II), no. 39

London, Trustees of the British Museum, Sloane Collection. Inv.
no. 5218/102

Dürer copied the *Primum Mobile* from the set of fifty Italian
engravings known as the *Tarocchi Cards*.[1] In spite of their name
(which is used for the sake of convenience) the Ferrarese prints
of *c.* 1465 were not packs of tarot cards, but rather constituted
a series of images made for educational games that are not fully
understood at present. The *Primum Mobile* was the forty-ninth
of the fifth set of ten. This fifth set represents the 'Ten Firmaments
of the Universe', the *Primum Mobile* itself being the last of the
material spheres, beyond the region of the fixed stars. This sphere
is in direct contact with God (the First Cause), and takes from
Him its infinite speed from which the lower spheres derive their
various slower motions. In the Ferrarese print (Fig. 4–1) as well
as in Dürer's copy, the concept of a sphere as prime mover is
represented by an angel, graced by movement and energy, holding the sphere she personifies as an attribute. Appropriately, the
sphere is free of stars and free of substance, to convey its
invisibility.

Dürer translated the severe engraved lines of his model into
rounded and lively three-dimensional forms which give the
figure an added sense of animation. By modulating the strength
of the penlines and by adding coloured washes, Dürer enlivened
the angel's dress, wings and hair.

Dürer copied twenty of the *Tarocchi*. A set of woodcut copies
of the *Tarocchi* was produced around 1493 in the shop of Michael
Wolgemut, Dürer's teacher. It was perhaps at that time that
Dürer first had the opportunity to copy the set of engravings.
However, the group of drawings after the *Tarocchi* which includes
the *Primum Mobile* has been dated a few years later, just before
Dürer's first journey to Italy.[2] The purpose of Dürer's copies
is not clear. There may have been a plan to replace the rather
stiff woodcuts from Wolgemut's studio with more lively ones.[3]

Dürer may well have remembered the image of the *Primum
Mobile*, the most lively and advanced of all the *Tarocchi*, a few
years later when engraving his justly famous *Large Fortune* (B. 77,
1501/02). The subject of the print is also based on an Italian
source, this time a written one, a poem by Angelo Poliziano
(1454–94). The figure of *Nemesis*, as Dürer characterized her,
recalls in pose and fluttering garment this *Primum Mobile*, and
creates the impression that Dürer linked the two concepts of
forces governing man's life sufficiently to borrow some formal
features of one for the other.

Urs Graf also copied the *Primum Mobile* but in reverse
(Fig. 4–2).[4] He enlivened and elaborated the figure further than

Fig 4-1 Master of the Tarocchi (E-series) *The Angel of the Ninth Sphere or
Primum Mobile*. National Gallery of Art, Washington, Ailsa Mellon Bruce
Fund

Fig 4-2 Urs Graf *Fortuna with a Phial*. Öffentliche Kunstsammlung, Kupferstichkabinett, Basel

Dürer turning her into a personification of Fortune, sporting a large feathered hat and sweeping windblown drapery, delineated in the slightly eccentric style of draughtsmanship typical of Urs Graf's work.

N.O.

1   This description of the *Primum Mobile* is quoted from Washington 1973, 156. This excellent catalogue provides a fundamental analysis of the *Tarocchi* and the problems they pose (Chapter VI, 'Masters of the Tarocchi', 81–157), and has been used extensively, with gratitude, for the present entry.

2   Dürer's drawings after the *Tarocchi* consist of two groups: ten drawn with a pointed pen, to which the copy of the *Primum Mobile* belongs, and eleven drawn with a broad-tipped pen. The first group is generally accepted as the earlier of the two. The authorship of the second group has been questioned. A summary of the various opinions is found in Winkler 1936, I, 90.

3   Winkler 1936, I, 90.

4   Öffentliche Kunstsammlung, Basel. See Maison 1966, 58, pl. 41. The *Tarocchi Cards* exist in two versions, referred to as E and S, E being the earlier one and S being based on E. Most prints of the S series are in mirror image. For the present drawing Dürer had access to a print from the E series (Hind 1938, I, E.I.49,a); Urs Graf must have copied from the S series (Hind 1938, I, E.I.49,b).

Albrecht Dürer

Nuremberg 1471–1528

5 Five Male Nudes

From Francesco Rosselli's engraving after Maso Finiguerra, *The Deluge*

Pen and black and grey ink
  188 × 206 mm
Provenance: G. Jurié; Endris (L. 812); A.F. von Lanna (L. 2773)
Bibliography: Weixlgärtner 1903, 89; Bock 1921, 34, no. 4444; Kauffmann 1924 (I), 60; Tietze-Conrat 1927, 89; Winkler 1939, IV, no. 890; Panofsky 1948, II, no. 1175; White 1971, no. 103; Strauss 1974, no. 1526/9; Anzelewsky and Mielke 1984, no. 119 (with further references)
Exhibition: Nuremberg 1971, no. 474

Berlin, Staatliche Museen Preussischer Kulturbesitz, Kupferstichkabinett. Inv. no. KdZ 4444

Fig 5-1 Francesco Rosselli after Maso Finiguerra *The Deluge*, (detail). Hamburger Kunsthalle, Kupferstichkabinett, Hamburg

Dürer transformed a group of figures from an earlier work of art to such an extent that it came as a surprise when Erica Tietze-Conrat established that Dürer had not freely sketched some figures for a representation of a Resurrection, but had copied five men on a raft from a fifteenth-century Florentine print by Francesco Rosselli after a design by Maso Finiguerra.[1] Dürer focussed on the comparatively small central motif in the middle distance of the elaborate print that depicts a multitude of episodes of the flood involving in total more than fifty figures (Fig. 5–2). The central motif in the print represents five men trying to save their lives on a raft (Fig. 5–1).

Dürer sketched all five figures. First he copied the two on the right in grey ink and then set down the other three and retouched the first two in black.[2] Dürer indicated the raft with a few lines but concentrated on the physical expression of boundless fear. In every detail, in the desperate gestures of hands and arms, in the clinging of feet and legs to the life-preserving raft, in the bending down of one frustrated figure (reversed from his counterpart in the print), and in the frenzied effort of the elderly man in the centre to flee to where there is no haven, in every single line, Dürer rethought the representation of the fear of imminent destruction. In the process, he removed the clothing of the Florentine figures and turned stiff puppets into animated humans.

The print was known in Germany to other artists as well, but apparently no one felt compelled to transform certain details in order to demonstrate the proper representation of a human condition that in the original was barely suggested. The drawing, very late in Dürer's career, came at a time when he was occupied with theoretical questions of expression.

N.O.

1   Tietze-Conrat 1927. The print, known in two versions, is listed and illustrated by Hind 1938, I, no. B. III.1 and 3. Here is illustrated an impression of B. III.1 which is discussed and attributed by K. Oberhuber in Washington 1973, 49, fig. 4–9.
2   Anzelewsky and Mielke 1984, no. 119.

5 Five Male Nudes

Fig 5-2 Francesco Rosselli after Maso Finiguerra *The Deluge*. Hamburger
Kunsthalle, Kupferstichkabinett, Hamburg

Fig 6-1 Albrecht Dürer *Flight into Egypt*. Rijksprentenkabinet, Amsterdam

Jan Swart van Groningen

Groningen *c.* 1500–Antwerp(?) after 1553

6 Flight into Egypt
After a woodcut by Dürer

Brush and pen and black ink and brush and brown ink, touches of red watercolour and brown wash, over sketch in black chalk divided into three parts by horizontal red chalk lines 400 × 322 mm
Annotated with pen and brown ink at bottom centre: *Bassan*
Provenance: Egmont
Bibliography: Eisler 1958, 86–87 [as by Hans von Kulmbach]; Haverkamp-Begemann and Logan 1970, no. 331, pl. 177

New Haven, Yale University Art Gallery, Library Transfer. Inv. no. 1961.61.22

In making a design for stained glass (indicated by the horizontal lines in red chalk), Jan Swart availed himself of the main figures in Dürer's woodcut, the *Flight into Eygpt* (B. 89) from the series the *Life of the Virgin*.[1] He fully transformed these figures (Fig. 6-1) by substituting strong outlines and broad washes for Dürer's more detailed woodcut. Furthermore, Swart situated the Holy Family in a northern European landscape of his own invention in contrast to Dürer's exotic tropical setting and substituted a column (from which an idol presumably would fall) for the ox, thereby exchanging one traditional motif of the *Flight into Egypt* for another.

Dürer's woodcuts generated great enthusiasm among Dutch and Flemish artists upon appearance – Dürer himself aided their distribution by presenting them as gifts during his trip to the Netherlands in 1520. Swart drew from Dürer on several occasions and thus shared with Lucas van Leyden, Pieter Coecke, Jan Gossaert and Bernard van Orley, the profound admiration for their German contemporary which is reflected in their paintings, drawings, and woodcuts.[2]

N.O.

---

1 Haverkamp-Begemann and Logan 1970, no. 331.
2 See Held 1931, 51–53.

6 Flight into Egypt

7 **Adam casting the Blame on Eve**

Pieter Coecke van Aelst

Aelst 1502–Brussels 1550

7 Adam casting the Blame on Eve

From the fresco by Baldassare Peruzzi in the Vault of the Cancelleria, Rome

Pen and brown ink and grey wash over black chalk, retouched by Rubens with brush and brown ink and ochre-white bodycolour
200 × 265 mm
Annotated with pen and brown ink at bottom right: *Mr Peter vanAel[st] 1540 va[. . .]*; with black chalk on *verso*: *Pieter Coecke van Aelst*
Provenance: N.A. Flinck; Sale, Sotheby's, London, 17 February 1960, no. 55 [as Dutch School, 16th century]
Bibliography: Van Regteren Altena 1962, 35; Müller-Hofstede 1965, 261–265; Jaffé 1966, 141, pl. 15; Marlier 1966, 303–304; Boon 1978, no. 132

Amsterdam, Rijksmuseum, Rijksprentenkabinet. Inv. no. 1960:83

From the spandrel fresco by Peruzzi (Fig. 7–1),[1] Coecke took over only the figures of Adam and Eve, retaining their positions, and placing them in a lightly suggested landscape. He omitted the figure of God the Father to whom Adam and Eve turn their gazes, he accusing her of being responsible for the fall of man. In spite of the skillful reworking by Rubens, who transformed the figures into his own robust versions of their Raphaelesque counterparts, the quick curved hatchings and loops in pen by Coecke's hand are clearly visible in the figures, in their hair, and in the bushes to either side of them.[2]

K.G. Boon has suggested that Coecke made this copy after Peruzzi when he was working on the publication of the books on architecture by Serlio who, as a student of Peruzzi, had inherited the drawings of his master. It is more likely, however, that Coecke copied Peruzzi's fresco before 1527, during the trip to Italy described by van Mander, who wrote that Coecke made many drawings of sculpture and architecture.[3] Coecke probably used these copies mainly as models for future figures and compositions. This clearly was the case with this copy. Echoes of both figures are found in a boy and woman in the foreground of Coecke's design for the tapestry *St. Paul preaching to the Macedonian Women*, in Munich (Fig. 7–2).[4]

N.O.

Fig 7-1 Baldassare Peruzzi *Adam accusing Eve before God*. Palazzo della Cancelleria, Rome

1   We are indebted to Anne-Marie Logan for generously making available to us her notes on this drawing.
2   Van Regteren Altena was the first to observe that the drawing (as by Gossaert) was retouched by Rubens (van Regteren Altena 1962, 35). Jaffé attributed the entire drawing to Rubens (Jaffé 1966, 141 and 1977, 49).
3   Boon 1978, no. 132. Müller-Hofstede was the first proponent of the earlier dating (Müller-Hofstede 1965, 261–265).
4   Staatliche Graphische Sammlung, Munich, inv. no. 1927:79; for the drawing, see Marlier 1966, 304, 314–315, fig. 252, and Wegner 1973, no. 35, pl. 7.

Fig 7-2 Pieter Coecke *St. Paul preaching to the Macedonian Women*. Staatliche
Graphische Sammlung, Munich

Il Parmigianino (Francesco Mazzola)

Parma 1503–Casalmaggiore 1540

8   School of Athens

After Raphael's fresco
Pen and brown ink, brown wash, over black chalk
235 × 415 mm
Verso: Various sketches in pen and brown ink
Provenance: Bonfiglioli of Bologna (?); Z. Sagredo (?); Consul Smith (?)
Bibliography: Parker 1939/40, 41–42, pl. 38; Popham and Wilde 1949, no. 598, fig. 131; Pope-Hennessy 1970, 224, fig. 208; Popham 1971, I, 19, 199, no. 666, II, pls. 205–206 (with further references)
Exhibition: London 1971 (I), no. 113

Windsor, Royal Library, Windsor Castle, lent by gracious permission of Her Majesty Queen Elizabeth II. Inv. no. 0533

In this drawing, Parmigianino copied Raphael's fresco, the *School of Athens* (Fig. 8–1), in the Vatican, completed in 1510. This copy is so studied and deliberate in its placement of figures and in the architectural indications that, as Parker suggested, the few but significant differences between this sheet and both Raphael's cartoon (Ambrosiana, Milan)[1] and the finished fresco itself, make it seem unlikely that Parmigianino was working from either. It appears more probable that he had access to a *modello* that does not exist anymore. Parker pointed out that both this drawing and the Ambrosiana cartoon omit the figure of the seated Heraclitus, placed so prominently in the fresco at the centre foreground.[2] Furthermore, in contrast to both the cartoon and the fresco, the figures are grouped in the drawing in a continuous line.[3] The composition of both the Ambrosiana cartoon and the fresco seem to be transformations of the one reflected in the present drawing and Parmigianino's model therefore may have been an earlier lost version.

In spite of Parker's doubts, the attribution of this sheet to Parmigianino seems correct. The attention paid to formal aspects rather than the emotional impact so important to Raphael's art, as well as the facial features only cursorily sketched and the elongated proportions are typically Parmigianinesque. When studying the entire oeuvre of Parmigianino as a draughtsman, Popham placed this drawing in the artist's Roman period (1524–27).[4]

As a draughtsman and painter, Parmigianino was influenced by Raphael.[5] A drawing of *Jesus Healing the Sick*, for a large fresco design, now in Angers, for example, shows how Parmigianino incorporated the composition and architectural settings of Raphael's Stanze frescoes, including the *School of Athens*, into his own work.[6]

J.C.

1   Knab et al. 1983, no. 362, repr.
2   Parker 1939/40, 42–43. He also believed that the relief representing Philosophy at the right in the fresco, which is also included in the drawing, was omitted from the cartoon. The cartoon, however, is cut off at that point and also, because of its condition, is difficult to read.
3   Pope-Hennessy 1970, 224.
4   Popham 1971, no. 666. Earlier, in the catalogue of drawings at Windsor (Popham and Wilde 1949, 248, no. 598), Popham had dated this sheet to Parmigianino's second Parma period (1531–39).
5   Popham 1971, 19–20.
6   Popham 1971, no. 5, pl. 189; Popham stated that the inscription on the *verso*: *fatto del Parmigianino da l'invenzione di Raffaello*, is an exaggeration.

8 School of Athens

Fig 8-1 Raphael *School of Athens*. Stanza della Segnatura, Vatican, Rome

9 Mercury and Cupid presenting Psyche to the Gods

Andrea Schiavone

Zara before 1501(?)–Venice 1563

9   Mercury and Cupid presenting Psyche to the Gods

After an engraving after Raphael

Pen and brown ink, brown wash, heightened with white, over
traces of black chalk, on brown-washed paper; laid down
374 × 603 mm

Fig 9-1 Raphael *Assembly of the Gods*, (detail). Villa Farnesina, Rome

Inscribed in pencil on *verso* of old mount: *Venus and Mercury sum-
moned before Jupiter and Juno/(Assembly of the Gods)/
Parmeggiano*
Provenance: C.R. Rudolf (L. 2811b)
Bibliography: Ballarin 1967, 89–90, fig. 103; Richardson 1976,
35–36, fig. 5; Richardson 1980, 8, 39, 129, no. 185, fig. 116;
Rearick 1980; no. 5, repr.; Bean et al. 1982, no. 236, repr.
Exhibitions: London-Birmingham-Leeds 1962, no. 62, pl. 3;
New York 1965, no. 116, repr.; London 1983, no. D53, repr.

New York, The Metropolitan Museum of Art, Rogers Fund,
1963. Inv. no. 63.93

Andrea Schiavone's drawing interprets, in reverse, Raphael's
fresco of the *Assembly of the Gods* in the Farnesina, completed in
1519 with the assistance of Giulio Romano, Luca Penni, and
others (Fig. 9–1). It differs from the fresco in many respects, and
corresponds more closely to an engraving that reproduces the
fresco in reverse and also includes changes (Fig. 9–2).[1] The
frieze-like parade of figures in the fresco became a denser, more
compact grouping in the engraving, while a few of the painted
figures were omitted. Schiavone has compressed his figures into
a narrower, but deeper space.

In the process of copying, Schiavone transformed the subject. At the right he substituted Pegasus and Bellerophon for
Mercury welcoming Psyche to Olympus, and in the centre of
the composition Psyche is introduced to Jupiter by Mercury and
Amor. Venus and Mars, central in the print, are moved to the
right. Schiavone, therefore, changed the subject from 'The
Assembly of the Gods with Mercury presenting Psyche to

Fig 9-2 Jacopo Caraglio after Raphael *Assembly of the Gods*, Cabinet des Estampes, Geneva

Olympus' to 'The Assembly of the Gods with Mercury and Cupid presenting Psyche to Jupiter and Juno'. Furthermore, Schiavone substituted elongated and graceful creatures, their volume and movements conveyed by fluttering draperies, for Raphael's classical, semi-nude figures. In doing so he demonstrated the influence of Parmigianino. In fact, according to an old inscription on the mount, this sheet was once attributed to Parmigianino. Schiavone's broad, lively washes and vibrant heightening on prepared paper set this drawing far apart from the colourful fresco and the precise, linear engraving.

Richardson pointed out that, according to Ridolfi, Schiavone was commissioned to paint scenes from the life of Psyche for a ceiling at Castello di S. Salvatore near Susegana (Conegliano; now lost).[2] The shape of this drawing, a rectangle with rounded edges, compatible to a ceiling panel, may suggest that Schiavone made this in preparation for that purpose.[3] Richardson dated this drawing to the late 1540s when Schiavone had renewed his interest in Raphael.[4]

Raphael's Farnesina frescoes inspired many artists, and were copied frequently, either directly or through the intermediary of engravings. François Perrier etched both the *Banquet of the Gods* and the *Assembly* giving it a more frieze-like feeling than Schiavone's copy.[5] Individual figures from the frescoes were also copied. The seated male nude seen from behind in the *Assembly* was copied by Jean Boucher in red chalk in 1600[6] and the figure of Psyche was copied by Charles Le Brun in black chalk (in reverse and therefore from a print).[7]

J.C.

1   B. XV.89.54 lists this engraving as by Jacopo Caraglio; others since Vasari have thought it was by Agostino Veneziano with the help of Marco Dente da Ravenna. Another drawing by Schiavone after the Farnesina fresco, *The Banquet of the Gods* (Richard and Trude Krautheimer Collection, Richardson 1980, no. 184), while sketchier than the present drawing, is not an exact copy either and likewise, is in reverse. Schiavone most likely copied this, as well, from an engraving (B. XV.43.14) published by Salamanca in 1545.

2   Ridolfi 1648, pt. I, 237, as cited by Richardson 1967, 36.

3   Bean et al. 1982, no. 236. McTavish in London 1983, no. D53 points out that Schiavone had also taken up the theme of Cupid and Psyche in two paintings, one in the Metropolitan Museum of Art, New York and the other in the Palazzo Strozzi, Florence.

4   Richardson 1980, 39, 42. Ballarin 1967, 89–90 dated this earlier, from the first half of that decade. Richardson 1976, 38 n. 29 suggested that Firenzuola's translation of the antique source for the story of Cupid and Psyche, Apuleius's *The Golden Ass*, which was not published in Venice until 1550, may be relevant in the dating of the ceiling paintings and thus the drawing.

5   Robert-Dumesnil 1842, VI, 33–34.

6   Musée du Louvre, inv. no. RF 35.515; see Paris 1983/84, no. 27.

7   Musée du Louvre, inv. no. RF 27.832; see Paris 1983/84, no. 146.

Jacopo Tintoretto

Venice 1518–1594

10 Reclining Figure personifying Day
After Michelangelo's sculpture

Black chalk, heightened with white, on blue paper
350 × 505 mm
Verso: Study of *Day*
Provenance: Purchased in London in 1954
Bibliography: Virch 1956, 111–116; Byam Shaw 1976, I, 205
    under no. 762; Bean et al. 1982, 242–243

New York, The Metropolitan Museum of Art, Rogers Fund,
    1954. Inv. no. 54.125 *recto*

According to Tintoretto's seventeenth-century biographer, Carlo Ridolfi, the artist inscribed on his studio wall, 'Il disegno di Michel Angelo, e'l colorito di Titiano'.[1] While this account may not be literally true, Tintoretto did make numerous studies after sculptures by Michelangelo and other Florentines and often quoted their figures in his paintings. Tintoretto is said never to have travelled to Florence, however, and seems to have relied on models or copies for his knowledge of Tuscan sculpture.[2]

He seems to have been particularly interested in the sculptures for the Medici Chapel.[3] It is documented that he owned models of both *Giuliano de' Medici*[4] and the four *Allegories of Time*, and that on at least one occasion he sketched Michelangelo's own wax study for the head of *St. Damian*.[5] Tintoretto, it is said, even showed himself holding a statuette of *Night* in an early self-portrait, now lost.[6]

Ridolfi, moreover, records that Tintoretto made

> an infinite number of drawings of [models of Michelangelo's *Allegories of Time*] by the light of an oil lamp so that he could compose in a powerful and solidly modelled manner by means of those strong shadows cast by the lamp.[7]

Only four drawings of *Evening*[8] and five of *Day*[9] survive; all in black chalk heightened with white, a technique perfectly suited to rendering 'those strong shadows'. The drawings record the figures from uncharacteristic views; most show the sculptures radically foreshortened. The drawings of *Day* (Fig. 10–1), for instance, include two views from above looking down the figure from the legs to the head, and one view of *Day* from behind and above his left shoulder.[10]

Both the *recto* and *verso* of the sheet here exhibited show a model of *Day* seen at an angle from the back. The model Tintoretto used differs from Michelangelo's sculpture since, as can be seen in his drawing, the bottom half of the figure was completed and details of hair, drapery and musculature were more fully worked out than in Michelangelo's original.

Moreover, we can be certain that Tintoretto drew not Michelangelo's *modello*, but a copy made some time after *Day* had been carved. It is well known that Michelangelo carved *Day* and *Night* before he had determined the architecture of the sarcophagus on which they rest. As a result, the bases of their sculpture-blocks do not conform to the curvature of the lid of the sarcophagus.[11] In Tintoretto's drawing, on the other hand, the lower outline of *Day*'s body clearly implies the arch of the lid rather than the base of the block.

10 Reclining Figure personifying Day

This rectification of sculpture and support is found in a terra-cotta copy of *Day* made by Michelangelo's assistant, Tribolo, in 1534.[12] Tribolo fashioned wax copies of all the figures in the Medici Chapel, presumably for reproduction. Tintoretto may very well have used a Tribolo copy as his direct source.

The dating of Tintoretto's studies after Michelangelo is problematic.[13] Ridolfi says Tintoretto copied statuettes of the *Allegories* made by Daniele da Volterra in 1557.[14] Tintoretto, however, certainly knew the sculptures before 1548 when he quoted *Evening* in the *Miracle of the Slave*.[15] On stylistic grounds, too, the drawings after the *Allegories* are generally placed in the middle to late 1540s. Presumably, the sheet in the Metropolitan would have originated, with the other studies, in this period.

Michelangelo's painted and sculpted figures both suggested to Tintoretto the means by which he could render the human form in movement without sacrificing its solidity. Elaborating upon both the complex poses and pronounced muscularity of the figures, Tintoretto brought out by means of daring viewpoints and strong illumination the mannerist qualities already present in the later work of Michelangelo which became an integral part of his artistic vocabulary for the duration of his career.

A.B.

Fig 10-1 Michelangelo Buonarroti *Day*. Medici Chapel, Florence

1   Ridolfi 1648, pt. II, 14.

2   Tintoretto's collection and use of casts is well attested to by all his early biographers, including his contemporary, Borghini. For discussion of this evidence, with further references, see especially Tietze and Tietze-Conrat 1944, 268–271 and Rossi 1975, 1–6.

3   See Coffin 1951 for the most extensive analysis of this.

4   As recorded in such drawings as those at Christ Church, Oxford, inv. nos. 0354 and 0355; see Byam Shaw 1976, 204, cat. nos. 759 and 760.

5   Gilbert 1961 and Smith 1981.

6   According to Ridolfi, as quoted by Virch 1956, 111.

7   Ridolfi 1648, pt. II, 14. This translation is from Ridolfi/Engass 1984, 14.

8   Uffizi, Gabinetto dei Disegni, Florence, inv. no. 13048F *recto* and *verso*; see Rossi 1975, figs. 38 and 39; and Collection of Count Seilern, London, no. 100 *recto* and *verso*, see Rossi 1975, figs. 13 and 14.

9   Besides the *recto* and *verso* of the sheet exhibited here, the others are: Christ Church, Oxford, inv. no. 0356 *recto* and *verso*, see Byam Shaw 1976, 205, cat. no. 262; and Musée du Louvre, Cabinet des Dessins, inv. no. 5384, see Rossi 1975, fig. 40.

10 Presumably, Tintoretto chose such views for two principal reasons. On the one hand, the studies permitted Tintoretto to emulate Michelangelo without directly, or at least overtly, copying him. On the other hand, the strong foreshortening of the figures would adapt them for use in the deep and rapid perspectives of his paintings.

11 See Pope-Hennessy 1985, 14–25, 327–339, for a discussion of the sculpture in the Medici Chapel.

12 See Wiles 1932 for this and other works by Tribolo after or influenced by Michelangelo.

13 Tietze and Tietze-Conrat 1944, 268–271; Rossi 1975, 1–6.

14 Ridolfi 1648, pt. II, 14.

15 This was first noticed by Coffin 1951, 122.

Fig 11-1 Michelangelo Buonarroti *Moses*. San Pietro in Vincoli, Rome

Hendrick Goltzius

Mühlbrecht 1558–Haarlem 1617

11 Moses
After Michelangelo's sculpture

Black chalk on grey-blue Venetian paper; heightened with
   white; outlines traced for transfer
   410 × 250 mm
Verso: Sketch of a head in black and white chalk
Bibliography: Reznicek 1961, no. 232, pl. 185; Maison 1966, 47,
   pl. 20
Exhibition: Rotterdam-Haarlem 1958, no. 120

Haarlem, Teylers Museum. Inv. no. K III 16

This black chalk copy belongs to a group of drawings after
antique sculpture, executed by Goltzius during his six-month
stay in Italy from 1590 to 1591. In the exhibited drawing, as
in other studies from the same group, Goltzius was concerned
primarily with making a record of exemplary sculptures. Reznicek has interpreted these drawings as a 'sketchbook', but they
may have been intended as a self-sufficient collection of
drawings.[1]

Two pairs of identical copies by Goltzius, one in black on
blue-grey paper and the other in red chalk on white paper,
survive for ten pieces of sculpture, among them Goltzius's copy
of the *Hercules Farnese* (Cat. no. 12). Since the outlines of each
of the ten black chalk copies have been traced for transfer, and
since the two versions are identical in both pose and size, it seems
certain that the red chalk versions were prepared with the aid
of the corresponding black chalk drawings.[2] The latter were not,
however, intended solely as a kind of transfer template. The
subtle and careful rendering of interior detail in the drawing
exhibited here (as well as all the other black chalk drawings in
the series) is not necessary to provide the contours for the red
chalk copy. From the incisions found on this sheet one might
surmise that Goltzius made a more finished red chalk version,
and that this is no longer extant. One cannot be sure, however,
as it is possible that a later hand incised the drawing.

Goltzius's decision to include this modern sculpture
(Fig. 11–1) in what was essentially a *résumé* of the best-known
and admired classical sculpture in Italy reflects Michelangelo's
unique position in the sixteenth and seventeenth centuries. He
was generally considered the one modern artist capable of
equalling, and even surpassing the work of the ancients.[3]

See also the next entry.

C.M.

1   Reznicek 1961, 89–93. See also the next entry.
2   Miedema 1969, 76–78.
3   See Vasari as quoted in Reznicek 1961, 90 and 340 no. 183. See also
Haskell and Penny 1981, 5, 19.

11 Moses

Hendrick Goltzius

Mühlbrecht 1558–Haarlem 1617

12 Hercules Farnese
After the antique

Red chalk with outlines traced for transfer; the top corners cut
390 × 215 mm
Verso: Design lightly traced in black chalk from *recto*

Fig 12-1 *Hercules Farnese*. Museo Nazionale, Naples

Bibliography: Hirschmann 1919, 61; Hirschmann 1921, 58–60,
   no. 145; Miedema 1969, 76–78; Reznicek 1961, 92–93,
   no. 227, pl. 179
Exhibition: Boston-St. Louis 1981. no. 16

Haarlem, Teylers Museum. Inv. no. N 19

This red chalk drawing belongs to the same series, the so-called
'Roman Sketchbook', as Cat. no. 11.[1] Reznicek has described

12 Hercules Farnese

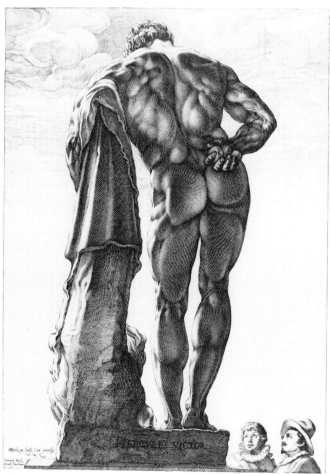

Fig 12-2 Hendrick Goltzius *Hercules Farnese*. Engraving. Teylers Museum, Haarlem

the nature and purpose of these drawings and his analysis, accepted by later authors, has shed much light on this remarkable set of drawings, yet leaves some questions unanswered.[2]

Reznicek argues that Goltzius intended to publish a series of prints of some of the most famous antiquities in Rome. Most of the black and red chalk drawings are of nearly identical size and represent the statues on a large scale. Of the twenty-seven sculptures copied, at least ten were drawn in two versions, one in black chalk and one in red chalk. The latter were brought to a very high degree of finish, as is the case with this drawing of the *Hercules Farnese* (Fig. 12–1). The rougher black chalk versions (Cat. no. 11) were, as Miedema convincingly demonstrated, transferred by tracing onto the white sheet for the red chalk version.[3]

In these greatly detailed, meticulously executed fair copies, Goltzius, as Reznicek observed, adopted the technique and precision of metal point as he had applied it previously to his portraits. It is likely that Goltzius made the red chalk drawings in Rome, rather than after his return, since some of this detail can hardly have been introduced from memory. The question remains: what was the purpose of this series? Reznicek assumed that Goltzius made them as designs for a series of prints. Indeed, three of the designs were published posthumously in 1617, from plates probably engraved by pupils.[4] Although in the case of the *Hercules Farnese* the red chalk version was probably used for the print (Fig. 12–2),[5] it seems unlikely that Goltzius needed the fair copies for making the engravings. He himself could have made these from the black chalk drawings. It seems more likely that Goltzius wished to make a set of drawings of classical sculpture as a self-sufficient, independent entity. Rather than considering this series a 'Sketchbook', Reznicek himself was not happy with this word;[6] one could call it Goltzius's 'Roman Portfolio'.[7]

C.M.

---

1   See previous entry.

2   Reznicek 1961, 89–94. I am greatly indebted to Professor Haverkamp-Begemann for sharing his ideas on this set of drawings.

3   Miedema 1969, 76–78 has published a useful concordance of these drawings after the antique.

4   Reznicek 1961, nos. 206, 208 and 227; for the authorship of the prints see under no. 227.

5   Miedema 1969, 75–78, figs. 1–3.

6   Reznicek 1961, 92.

7   One may surmise that Goltzius planned to draw all the sculptures in red chalk, but did not complete the task. Furthermore, one may wonder whether the 'portfolio' was intended for Rudolph II.

Hendrick Goltzius

Mühlbrecht 1558–Haarlem 1617

13 Portrait of Jan Govertsen as St. Luke the Evangelist
In the style of Dürer

Pen and brown ink on parchment
490 × 378 mm
Inscribed in the centre left: *H.G. 1614*
Bibliography: Reznicek 1961, 45, no. 70, pl. 442
Exhibition: Rotterdam-Haarlem 1958, no. 103

Veste Coburg, Kunstsammlungen der Veste Coburg. Inv. no. Z 2285

Goltzius portrayed Govertsen, a noted collector of seashells, in the manner of Albrecht Dürer. Four drawings by Goltzius of Govertsen survive. All postdate 1600 and are Düreresque, although none of them is based on a specific work by the sixteenth-century master.[1] The drawing here exhibited combines a variety of characteristics found in different drawings by Dürer. The relationship of the figure to the frame, the early sixteenth-century costume, the motif of the wall and the column behind the figure, the hair style, the gesture of the hands holding the pen and book, and even the sitter's features are all unquestionably 'Dürer-like'. At the same time Goltzius translated the master's engraving style (Fig. 13–1),[2] into his personal swelling-line pen technique that he developed for a number of drawings, most of them on parchment, in a *tour-de-force* demonstration of his ability to imitate engraving in a different medium.[3]

It is not known why either the artist or the sitter would have chosen an archaizing portrait style on four different occasions. Undoubtedly, both were participating in a contemporary 'Dürer-renaissance' which took place in The Netherlands and Germany, and especially at the Court of Rudolph II in Prague.[4]

In spite of Goltzius's effort to conjure up the image of Dürer and to apply a contrived, demanding technique to this portrait, he rendered the likeness of the sitter convincingly, to judge by the portrait Goltzius himself painted of Jan Govertsen as shell collector (Fig. 13–2)[5] in which there is a greater emphasis on verisimilitude.

C.M.

1   Reznicek 1961, nos. 273–275; See also Reznicek 1960, 39–41. The portrait of Govertsen in the British Museum, London, is more closely related to a specific work by Dürer (the engraved portrait of Willibad Imhoff of Nuremberg).
2   Cf. Dürer's portrait of *Willibald Pirckheimer*, B. VII, 106 (113). See also Reznicek 1961, 52–53.
3   Reznicek has written an excellent analysis of these 'Federkunststücke' (Reznicek 1961, 27, 28, 76, 77, 182, 183). Laetitia Smit is preparing a further study on these drawings.
4   After previous studies of the 'Dürer-renaissance' by Kauffmann and others, Reznicek provided a synthesis of this phenomemon (Reznicek 1961, 54, n. 15).
5   For the portrait of *Jan Govertsen as a Shell Collector*, see Reznicek 1960, 40, fig. 5.

13 Portrait of Jan Govertsen as St. Luke the Evangelist

Fig 13-2 Hendrick Goltzius *Portrait of Jan Govertsen as a Shell Collector*. Museum Boymans-van Beuningen, Rotterdam

Fig 13-1 Albrecht Dürer *Willibald Pirckheimer*

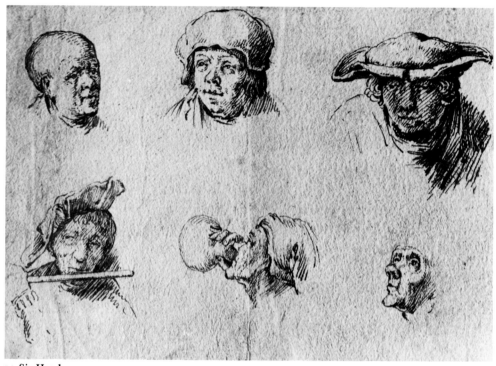

14 Six Heads

Jacques de Gheyn II

Antwerp 1565–The Hague 1629

14 Six Heads
From the *Dance of Mary Magdalene* by Lucas van Leyden

Pen and brown ink
94 × 137 mm
Provenance: J. de Grez

Fig 14-1 Lucas van Leyden *Dance of Mary Magdalene*. Rijksprentenkabinet, Amsterdam

Bibliography: Inventaire de Grez 1913, no. 1339; van Regteren Altena 1936, 97; van Regteren Altena 1983, II, no. 1042, pl. 374

Brussels, Musées Royaux des Beaux-Arts de Belgique. Inv. no. de Grez 1339

De Gheyn drew these six heads from the large engraving by Lucas van Leyden of 1519 (Fig. 14–1), spacing them on the page quite evenly with no relation to their relative placement in Lucas's print. This type of copy belongs to a tradition of drawings and prints that can be traced back to the fifteenth-century model books in which heads, arms, draperies, and other motifs were assembled in such categories on individual sheets of paper for later reference. Gerard David also took part in this tradition when he sketched four heads from van Eyck's *Ghent Altarpiece* on one sheet of paper in a similar fashion (Fig. 14–2).[1]

  In spite of maintaining the traditional grouping, Jacques de Gheyn seems to have copied these heads neither as a source of

Fig 14-2 Gerard David *Four Heads*, after details from the *Ghent Altarpiece*.
National Gallery of Canada, Ottowa

motifs to which he could revert when in need of a model, nor as a study of Lucas's style of engraving. For the latter purpose he would not have translated the sharp taut lines into short parallel strokes which indicate but do not imitate Lucas van Leyden's shapes and areas of light and shadow. Rather, he copied these heads for their expressive qualities. Jacques de Gheyn, himself greatly interested in the representation of emotions as conveyed in facial features, recognized the variety and depth of Lucas's understanding of man's feelings. Lucas distinguished himself from his contemporaries in this respect, as did Jacques de Gheyn from the majority of his own generation by recognizing that talent of Lucas.

See also the following entry.

N.O.

1   National Gallery of Canada, Ottawa, inv. no. 6986. Recently discussed and illustrated, with bibliographic references, in Washington-New York 1986/87, no. 44. On the development of model books see especially Jenni 1976 and Bolten 1985.

Jacques de Gheyn II

Antwerp 1565–The Hague 1629

15 The Triumph of Mordechai and Studies of Heads

From an engraving by Lucas van Leyden and three woodcuts by Albrecht Dürer

Pen and light brown ink; laid down
144 × 204 mm
Provenance: P. Crozat (L. 2951); Huquier père, Sale, Amsterdam, 14 September 1761, no. 2931 (to Fouquet); W. Argoutinsky-Dolgoroukoff (L. 2602 d)
Bibliography: Van Regteren Altena 1936, 97; van Regteren Altena 1983, II, no. 1041, pl. 34
Exhibition: The Hague 1952, no. 33

Amsterdam, Coll. I.Q. van Regteren Altena Heirs

In contrast to Cat. no. 14, here de Gheyn copied a group of figures and individual heads from several sources onto one page. The upper half of the sheet he used for Mordechai and his retinue, excising them from their entourage in Lucas van Leyden's engraving *The Triumph of Mordechai* (B. 32). He omitted Mordechai's horse and the man in the foreground who partly obscures the figures (Fig. 15–1). In the lower portion he placed six heads lifted from three woodcuts of Dürer's *Passion: The Last Supper* (B. 5), *Christ in Gethsemane* (B. 6) and *The Ecce Homo* (B. 9).

In this and the preceding drawing, both comparatively early works, de Gheyn faithfully copied motifs, translating shapes, light, and shade by means of a personal system of lively parallel striations which is typical of his own drawing style. The placement on the page is also personal. The two men at the bottom right corner might be seen as related to Mordechai in spite of their different scale. In that case men mocking Christ have been turned into bystanders honouring Mordechai.

This is not the only instance of an artist suggesting connections between seemingly random sketches on one page. Rembrandt made two Mughal princes from different miniatures face one another (Cat. no. 33) while Delacroix placed back to back a naiad and a river god from disparate sections of the same print (Cat. no. 59). Goya, on the other hand, had the crouching figure from one plate stand in for Caiaphas in a second plate in his own version of Flaxman's illustrations to Dante's *Divine Comedy* (Cat. no. 52), to cite only the few examples exhibited here.

The liberty taken with Lucas's linear vocabulary also found in the preceding entry and two other drawings after the same artist,[1] indicates that de Gheyn made these copies not merely to train his engraver's hand but rather for a broader involvement with the work of his distinguished and admired predecessor. Indeed de Gheyn's studies after Lucas van Leyden and Dürer coincide with a lively interest by other Dutch and particularly Haarlem artists in these two great print-makers of the sixteenth century.[2] De Gheyn and his teacher, Hendrick Goltzius, owed much to both.

See also the three preceding entries.
N.O.

[1]   Van Regteren Altena 1983, nos. 1041–1044.
[2]   See Reznicek 1961, 54 and van Regteren Altena 1983, I, 49.

15 The Triumph of Mordechai and Studies of Heads

Fig 15-1 Lucas van Leyden *The Triumph of Mordechai*. Rijksprentenkabinet,
Amsterdam

16 Draped Figures

Sir Peter Paul Rubens

Siegen 1577–Antwerp 1640

16 Draped Figures

After Tobias Stimmer

Pen and brown ink
   207 × 136 mm
Provenance: Count G.A. Sparre; Count J.G. de la Gardie;
   Count P. de la Gardie
Bibliography: Magnusson 1977, 78, pl. 7; Belkin 1984, 202,
   204–205
Exhibition: Basel 1984, no. 96

Stockholm, Nationalmuseum. Inv. no. 572/1973

In his *Teutsche Akademie* (1675), Joachim von Sandrart recounted a conversation which he had with Rubens on the boat from Utrecht to Amsterdam in which he praised the work of Stimmer. Rubens, who also admired the sixteenth-century master, thereby admitted to having copied many of Stimmer's biblical woodcuts in his youth.[1] This passage confirmed Frits Lugt's identification in 1943 of a group of anonymous drawings as copies by Rubens after German and Dutch sixteenth-century prints.[2] Twelve sheets of nearly the same dimensions with copies after Joost Amman and Hendrick Goltzius as well as Stimmer are now known, the Stockholm sheet exhibited here has been recognized most recently.[3]

Onto a single sheet Rubens would randomly place individual figures or groups of figures, selecting those of similar type from more than one print. Belkin suggests that Rubens may have had model books (Fig. 16–1), in the back of his mind when compiling these sheets of studies.[4] His practice here differs markedly from that in his earliest copies, after Holbein's *Dance of Death*, which reproduce the original designs in their entirety.[5]

In the Stockholm drawing, Rubens assembled figures from four woodcuts (Figs. 16–2 to 16–5) which like all other copies from Stimmer are taken from the Old Testament portion of the *Neue Künstliche Figuren Biblischer Historien* (1576). Rubens copied the details accurately, with the exception of the group of three men in the bottom left corner taken from the scene depicting 'Jacob's Son at the Death Bed of his Father'. Here, Rubens compressed a group of six figures into three by eliminating three in the centre and moving the outer figures closer to each other. This reshuffling indicates that in this case Rubens worked on the page from right to left.[6]

The pen and ink technique used in this sheet captures the feeling of the graphic medium without imitating it line for line, as also in Cat. no. 17. Although this is a student work, the technique is highly accomplished, especially in the outline figure at upper left. Already then Rubens was able to maintain the coherence of the figure with minimal means.[7] Rubens rarely reused Stimmer's figures in his later work, but this encounter with the earlier master's work did introduce Rubens to a more massive figure style and move him to a more profound understanding of gesture and expression.[8]

   C.M.

Fig 16-1 Master of the Coburg Rondels *Drapery Studies*. Graphische Sammlung der Staatsgalerie, Stuttgart

Fig 16-2 Tobias Stimmer Illustration from the *Neue Künstliche Figuren Biblischer Historien*. Universitätsbibliothek, Basel

Fig 16-3 Tobias Stimmer Illustration from the *Neue Künstliche Figuren Biblischer Historien*. Universitätsbibliothek, Basel

1   Lugt 1943, 99–100, 114 n. 2. This conversation probably took place in 1627 when Rubens visited Holland.
2   Lugt 1943, 99–106.
3   Magnusson 1977, 78, pl. 7. Basel 1984, no. 66, and pls. 112–145 for a complete list of sources, and nos. 98–99.
4   Belkin 1984, 203; see also Maurer 1985, 85–86. On the model books, see C. Andersson, 'Excursis: The Master of the Coburg Rondels', in Detroit etc. 1981/82, 388–398 and fig. 25. See also Cat. nos. 14, 17 and 22 of the present exhibition and the literature referred to there.
5   Van Regteren Altena 1977.
6   Basel 1984, nos. 92–103.
7   As in the opinion of Held 1959, I, 63, no. 1; Belkin 1984, 205.
8   Lugt 1943, 106–108; Belkin 1984, 205–206; Held 1986, 45, no. 5.

Fig 16-4 Tobias Stimmer Illustration from the *Neue Künstliche Figuren Biblischer Historien*. Universitätsbibliothek, Basel

Fig 16-5 Tobias Stimmer Illustration from the *Neue Künstliche Figuren Biblischer Historien*. Universitätsbibliothek, Basel

17 Two Hornblowers

Sir Peter Paul Rubens

Siegen 1577–Antwerp 1640

17 Two Hornblowers
From two engravings after Stradanus

Pen and brown ink
  140 × 151 mm

Fig 17-2 Adriaen Collaert after Johannes Stradanus *Encomium Musices, no. 12*, (detail). Rijksprentenkabinet, Amsterdam

Fig 17-3 Adriaen Collaert after Johannes Stradanus *Encomium Musices, no. 13*, (detail). Rijksprentenkabinet, Amsterdam

Provenance: C. Rogers (L. 625); W. Young Ottley; Sir T. Lawrence (L. 2445); R.P. Roupell; V. Koch; F. Koenigs (L. Suppl. 2023a)

Bibliography: Jaffé 1956, 318; Burchard and d'Hulst 1963, no. 4

Exhibitions: Amsterdam 1933, no. 109; Rotterdam 1938, no. 343; Rotterdam 1939, no. 27; Paris 1952, no. 37; Rotterdam 1952, no. 62; Antwerp 1956, no. 28

Rotterdam, Museum Boymans-van Beuningen. Inv. no. V 93

Fig 17-1 Studio of Sir Peter Paul Rubens *The Bear Hunt*, (detail). North Carolina Museum of Art, Raleigh. Purchased with Funds from the State of North Carolina

The musicians in this drawing are taken from two consecutive prints, nos. 12 and 13 (Figs. 17–2, 17–3), in a series of eighteen which depict hymns and scenes from the Old Testament with music as the central theme. Published by Philip Galle, the *Encomium Musices* was engraved by Adriaen Collaert, in 1589, after drawings by Stradanus.[1] Rubens selected figures of a similar type from the left foreground of each print, disregarding their original narrative context and concentrating solely on the upper part of the figures.

The use of pen and ink may have been inspired by the technique of engraving; the hatching does not, however, reproduce the original shading with complete accuracy. This is true of many pen and ink copies from the 1590s as, for example, Rubens's copies after Stimmer (Cat. no. 16).

Already in the years preceding his departure for Italy, Rubens had an interest in the motif of blowing a horn and the human energy involved in it. Later he would repeatedly paint hornblowers and trumpeters in his hunting scenes, triumphs and other subjects. One particularly vigorous hornblower, this time seen full face, is found in *The Bear Hunt* in the North Carolina Museum of Art, Raleigh, which Rubens painted with Frans Snyders and other members of his studio (Fig. 17–1).[2]

C.M.

1   Jaffé established this source in 1956. The prints are listed by Hollstein 1949, 201, nos. 18–36.
2   Balis 1986, no. 27.

Fig 18-1 Sir Peter Paul Rubens *The Spinario*. Trustees of the British Museum, London

Sir Peter Paul Rubens

Siegen 1577–Antwerp 1640

18 The Medici Madonna (detail)
After Michelangelo's sculpture

Black chalk; laid down
   200 × 278 mm
Provenance: R. Cosway; D. Laing; Royal Scottish Academy
Bibliography: Jaffé 1966, 145 n. 22; Jaffé 1977, 20; Andrews 1985, no. D 712, fig. 470
Exhibition: London 1966, no. 39

Edinburgh, National Gallery of Scotland. Inv. no. D. 712

Rubens first came in direct contact with the work of Michelangelo upon his arrival in Italy. The large number of copies which mark this first encounter reflect the range and extent of Rubens's immediate response to the venerated master's work – a response that would affect Rubens's work for the duration of his artistic career.[1] Jaffé tentatively dates this drawing to 1600 when Rubens, on his way to Rome, passed through Florence where he sketched the *Medici Madonna* (Fig. 18–2), located then, as it is now, in the Medici Chapel of San Lorenzo.[2]

Rubens concentrated on the Christ Child. On the right side of the sheet, he sketched the Child quickly, accurately rendering the motif. On the left side, he provided his own variation, seeing the sculpture more from the left, articulating the limbs and lending more life to the Child. He shifted the Virgin's left leg, which in the original provides a firm base for the Child, outward. As the *pentimenti* in the Child's left leg make clear, Rubens made a concerted effort to establish the proper, new position for this leg. Without it, the Infant would have been suspended even more precariously between His Mother's legs than He is in the original. In this transformation of Michelangelo's sculpture, Rubens sought to emphasize the Child's energetic embrace of His Mother.

Rubens juxtaposed an accurate rendering of another sculpture, *The Spinario*, or perhaps a model assuming its pose, and its free adaptation in a similar way on a sheet in the British Museum of approximately the same date (Fig. 18–1).[3] On the left, he made the boy (who in the original is concentrating on extracting a thorn from his foot) lift his head to confront the viewer as if to suggest that he has just been interrupted.

The subject of the Madonna and Child occupied Rubens throughout his life. In no painting did he adopt the pose of Michelangelo's sculpture literally, but echoes of his acquaintance with it are noticeable in works made as far apart as the *Holy Family* of *c.* 1617 in Potsdam and the *Mystic Marriage of St. Catherine* of *c.* 1635 in Toledo, Ohio.[4]

   C.M.

1   Jaffé 1977, 19–22.
2   Pope-Hennessy 1985, 14–25, 327–339.
3   Burchard and d'Hulst 1963, no. 16.
4   Oldenbourg 1921, 139 and 343.

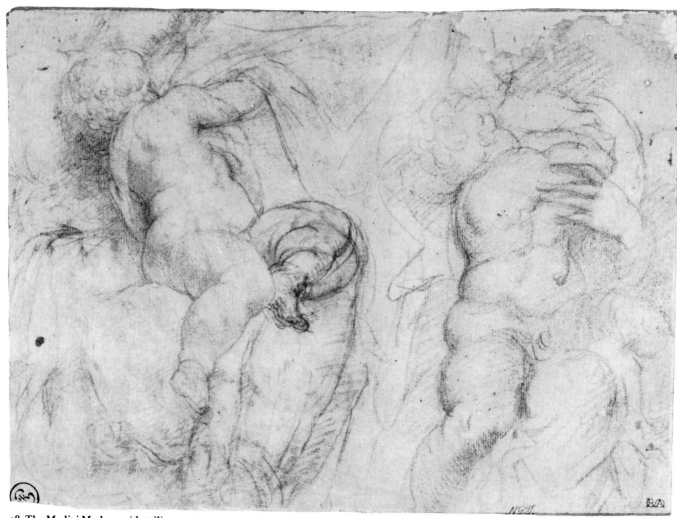

18 The Medici Madonna (detail)

Fig 18-2 Michelangelo Buonarroti *Medici Madonna*, Medici Chapel,
Florence

19 Pan reclining

Sir Peter Paul Rubens

Siegen 1577–Antwerp 1640

19 Pan reclining

After the sixteenth-century Italian sculpture

Red and black chalk, retouched and reworked with brush and bright red and reddish brown ink, heightened and corrected with white, touches of brush and greenish bodycolour (lower left in grapes, leaf, branch) and brownish bodycolour (at left

Fig 19-1 Giovanni Montorsoli *Reclining Pan*. The Saint Louis Art Museum, Museum Purchase

in leaf, branches, hoof of Pan); also touches of red chalk on top of other, primarily brown colours; the black chalk background covered with a transparent, partly greyish wash which has slightly oxidized at edges of the sheet

310 × 493 mm

Provenance: J. Richardson Sr. (L. 2184); B. West (L. 419); Sir C. Grenville (L. 549); Earl of Warwick (L. 2600); Sir J.C. Robinson (L. 1433); Sale, Christie's, London, 12–14 May 1902, no. 352; C.A. de Burlet; L. Burchard; W. Burchard; Sale, Sotheby's, London, 9 April 1970, no. 63; A. Delon; Colnaghi, London (1977)

Bibliography: Glück and Haberditzl 1928, 25, pl. 25 [drawn in Rome 1601–08, after antique sculpture]; Bethe 1930/31, 182, repr.; Jungmaker 1938, 133, fig. 72 [in reverse]; Jaffé 1954, 135–136, repr. [offset of early drawing by Rubens, worked up by him in last decade of his life]; Jaffé 1956, 317; Held 1959, 50, 52; Haverkamp-Begemann et al. 1964, 23 [entire drawing dates from *c.* 1605–08]; Jaffé 1965, 381, no. 161; Müller-Hofstede 1966, 452, no. 161; Stechow 1968, 39–40; Logan and Haverkamp-Begemann 1978, 449, no. 65; Möseneder 1979, 138–139, fig. 51; Held 1986, no. 40, pl. 29 [*c.* 1605–08]; Logan 1987

Exhibitions: Siegen 1927, no. 19; Amsterdam 1933, no. 101, repr. [offset of drawing made by Rubens in Italy, reworked by Rubens later in Antwerp]; Brussels 1938/39. no. 7, [*idem*, reworked after 1630, perhaps for print]; Rotterdam 1939, no. 7, pl. VII [*idem*]; London 1953, no. 272 [*idem*; only drawing in red chalk was offset, according to Burchard]; London 1953/54, no. 521 [*idem*]; Antwerp 1956, no. 121, pl. 161 and under no. 19 [similar to counter-proof of *Ignudo*, drawn *c.* 1630–40 over counter-proof of drawing of 1601–08]; Paris 1974, no. 88; London 1976, no. 42, repr.; London 1977, no. 38a, repr. [early 1630s?]; Washington 1978 (III), 65, repr.

Washington, National Gallery of Art, Ailsa Mellon Bruce Fund. Inv. no. 1978.17.1 (B-30457)

The drawing is a free copy of the marble sculpture made by a Florentine sculptor of the sixteenth century, perhaps Giovanni Montorsoli or Vincenzo Rossi, possibly by recutting a classical sculpture.[1] At least by 1627, when it was copied in terracotta,[2] the sculpture (The Saint Louis Art Museum) was in the Barberini collections where it served as a fountain.[3] It represents Pan holding his pipes, lying on his back.

Copying the sculpture from an elevated vantage point, Rubens deviated from the model in several respects (Fig. 19–1). He replaced the rocks on which Pan rests his hooves with a tangle of grape-vines thereby expanding the motif of the single vine-stalk in the foreground of the sculpture. The classical belief that the musical, wine-loving god of cattle took a rest at noon, when he should not be disturbed if his anger was to be avoided may explain why Rubens emphasized the vines. As Pan twists to face outwards, Rubens introduced tension to the torso and emphasized the musculature of the body and the texture of the skin. These differences are in keeping with his manner of copying from the antique.[4] The most notable change, however, is that drawing and sculpture are each other's mirror image.

Although in its finished state the drawing has all the characteristics of an immediate sketch, it must have been executed in a number of stages. The red and black chalk-lines that lie directly on the paper and which first defined the subject must have been derived by counter-proofing from an earlier, probably rather summary, version, now lost, in which Rubens represented the sculpture as it appeared to him.[5] He subsequently reworked this 'offset' with the brush in various tints of red and brown, and with red chalk. Rubens did this so extensively that little of the counter-proofed first stage remains visible.[6]

The reworking of the drawing as well as the colour of the red brush strokes are paralleled in various drawings by Rubens which he made or retouched during his stay in Italy, particularly *Three Nude Women* after Primaticcio (Rotterdam), the so-called *Niccolò da Uzzano* (Morgan Library, New York), the *Standing Man* after Correggio (Musée du Louvre), and the *Ignudo* after Michelangelo, also a reworked counter-proof (London). This *Pan reclining* probably also dates from his stay in Italy (1601–1608).

Although virtually a Renaissance sculpture, the *Barberini*

Faun was admired in the seventeenth century as one of the major classical sculptures. In 1626 or somewhat earlier Cornelis Poelenburgh made two drawings after it which were published by Jan de Bisschop in 1671 among his prints after *exempla* of classical sculpture which included the *Crouching Aphrodite*, the *Torso Belvedere*, and the *Two Wrestlers*. In 1675, Joachim von Sandrart reproduced the sculpture in a series of illustrations of classical sculptures in his *Teutsche Akademie*. The sculpture kept its fame, although by the time Winckelmann wrote about classical sculpture (1764) it apparently was recognized as a Renaissance piece.[7] In 1722, when writing about works of art in the Palazzo Barberini, Jonathan Richardson listed it as an 'Antique', and commented: 'A fine Satyr lying, Marble: my father has a large Drawing of this, highly finish'd by *Rubens. Biscop* has it No. 57,58', thereby referring to the very drawing here exhibited.[8]

E.H.-B.

1   Friedrich Kriegbaum, in Bethe 1930/31, supposed that the sculpture could be a work of Vincenzo Rossi. Jaffé 1965, 381, no. 161, suggested that the authorship of Montorsoli was not certain, and that the sculpture was recut second-century work.
2   The anonymous terracotta copy in Dresden is inscribed: *BARBERUN ANO 1627 IN ROMA DEN 140 APRIL* (Bethe 1930, 183); in 1632 it was inventoried by Nicolò Menghini (Lavin 1975, 133, no. 81).
3   Möseneder 1979, 131–141, figs. 46, 51.
4   Fubini and Held 1964 and Muller 1982.
5   Ever since Burchard, in Bethe 1930/31, introduced the notion of a counterproof in connection with this drawing, commentators have considered one or another stage of the drawing as a counter-proof.
6   The clarity and freshness of the counter-proof suggests that Rubens pulled the 'offset' immediately after he had made that initial sketch. In it he apparently had defined the sculpture just enough to continue his interpretation without benefit of the sculpture itself. This would explain why he turned the legs and feet of the buckhide on the chest of Pan into straps with leaf-like attachments.
7   Poelenburgh's drawings are lost, but Jan de Bisschop's etchings are inscribed *Pool.del.* (van Gelder and Jost 1985, 142–143; Logan 1987). Poelenburgh left Rome in 1626 which provides a date *ante quem*. Sandrart 1679, II, pt. 2, 13. The date of the drawing Sandrart used (one of his own?) is not known. Winckelmann simply did not mention the sculpture.
8   Richardson 1722, 164.

Sir Peter Paul Rubens

Siegen 1577–Antwerp 1640

20 Hercules and the Nemean Lion
After woodcuts by Boldrini and Vicentino after Raphael

Red chalk, brush and red ink, yellow chalk, heightened and corrected with white gouache and touches of black chalk; laid down; upper right corner made up
318 × 484 mm
Provenance: P.J. Mariette (L. 1852); Sir T. Lawrence (L. 2445); Colnaghi
Bibliography: Burchard and d'Hulst 1963, 305 under no. 192; Haverkamp-Begemann et al. 1964, no. 20
Exhibitions: London 1835, no. 31; Williamstown 1960, no. 428; London 1977, no. 63

Williamstown, Sterling and Francine Clark Art Institute. Inv. no. 922

Haverkamp-Begemann dates this work to the second half of Rubens's stay in Italy.[1] The group itself (which depicts one of the Ten Labours of Hercules) derives from Greco-Roman reliefs and antique coins. Rubens probably knew this motif from a pair of woodcuts executed by Vicentino and Boldrini after Raphael's designs (Figs. 20–1, 20–2).[2]

Rubens combined elements from both: the large scale of man and beast in one with the horizontal format of the other.[3] He reproduced the feeling of the Venetian landscape of each without adhering to detail. Rubens, however, rethought the main subject itself; he changed the lion from a profile to a frontal view, and reformulated the animal's right leg only after the landscape had been sketched in. This change resolves a certain awkwardness in the earlier versions by interlocking the two figures in space rather than in a frieze-like manner across the surface. Furthermore, he reproportioned the body of Hercules and the volumes of combatants, emphasizing the size of Hercules. *Pentimenti* in the hero's lower back indicate Rubens's struggle to lend vigour, vitality and intensity to the two protagonists.

The same group with some significant changes appears in a drawing of *c.* 1612–16 (Fig. 20–3). Although Rubens didn't use this exact motif in later works, adaptations of the animal's pose can be found in two of the large *Lion Hunts*, one of *c.* 1615 in the Gemäldegalerie, Dresden and another of *c.* 1616/17 in the Alte Pinakothek, Munich.[4]

C.M.

1   Haverkamp-Begemann et al. 1964, no. 20.
2   Haverkamp-Begemann et al. 1964, figs. 20–22. Held suggests (1986, under no. 97) that Rubens might also have been looking at a panel designed by Giulio Romano for the *Sala dei Cavalli* in the Palazzo del Te, Mantua (Hartt 1958, pl. 185). Because this is executed in *grisaille*, without even a suggestion of landscape in the background, the Vicentino and Boldrini woodcuts appear to be a more likely source.
3   Held 1986, no. 97. In Rubens's sheet of studies (Held 1986, no. 217) in London, the Hercules/Lion group reappears twice, in light outline. Another version of just this group as represented in the drawing exhibited here, undoubtedly by Rubens himself, is in the Louvre. Watteau copied one or the other in a red chalk drawing of nearly the same dimensions. See Haverkamp-Begemann et al. 1964, under no. 20.
4   Oldenbourg 1921, 113 and 154.

20 Hercules and the Nemean Lion

Fig 20-1 Nicolò Boldrini (attrib.) *Hercules and the Nemean Lion*

Fig 20-2 Giuseppe Rossigliani, called Nicolò Vicentino *Hercules and the Nemean Lion*. Museum of Fine Arts, Boston, Bequest of W.G. Russell Allen

Fig 20-3 Sir Peter Paul Rubens *Hercules and the Nemean Lion*. Cabinet des Estampes, Antwerp

Sir Peter Paul Rubens

Siegen 1577–Antwerp 1640

21 Israelites wrestling with Giant Snakes
From Michelangelo's fresco

Initial drawing in pen and wash, pasted down, reworked, cut up, rearranged on main sheet and filled out in brush and brown wash, white and grey body colour and black chalk; top corners repaired
385 × 596 mm
Provenance: Sir T. Lawrence; King William II of Holland; G. Leembruggen; Malcolm
Bibliography: Hind 1923, II, 7, no. 4; Hoff 1938, 14–16; Fubini and Held 1964, 125, pl. 3
Exhibition: London 1977, no. 16

London, Trustees of the British Museum. Inv. no. 1895-9-15-1055

Rubens frequently reworked drawings by other artists, occasionally to such an extent that they became the basis for entirely new and different works as in the drawing here exhibited.[1]

In this case he started with a pen drawing by an unknown artist, which probably represented, in its entirety, Michelangelo's fresco of *The Brazen Serpent* (Fig. 21–1) in the spandrel located in the northwest corner of the Sistine Chapel, immediately above the *Last Judgement*. Rubens first pasted it down, then reworked it, cut it into pieces and rearranged them over a larger surface, altering details and filling in where necessary to complete figures or motifs. He used only the figures overwhelmed by the snakes represented in the right-hand, northern side of the spandrel, omitting those that rescued themselves by gazing at the serpent in the left-hand, southern section, and the brazen serpent itself. The man with the prominent, well-muscled back was kept intact, whereas the second prominent body in the foreground, curled up in a fetal position, was halved and given a new torso, now stretching out prostrate in the left corner. The man bending forward, fighting a serpent which winds itself about his leg and neck, is retained almost entirely. His left leg, obscured in the original, was completed by Rubens.

In reworking the drawing and by omitting the brazen serpent entirely, Rubens changed the subject to represent Israelites overwhelmed by giant snakes in punishment for their blasphemy of Jehovah.[2]

Rubens may have made this drawing towards the end of his stay in Italy. Rowlands points out that Rubens executed a *Brazen Serpent* (formerly in the collection of Count Antoine Seilern, London, now in the Courtauld Institute Galleries, London) shortly after his return to Antwerp in 1608, and that he may have had this drawing in mind, although the relationship between the two is not direct.[3] An anonymous copy of the British Museum drawing was bound as the first leaf in the volume of copies after Rubens's own copies after the antique (preserved in Milan).[4] Although it does not prove that Rubens executed the drawing here exhibited during his Italian sojourn, it lends support to this hypothesis.

Michelangelo and classical antiquity – probably in that order of intensity – mesmerized Rubens throughout his life

21 **Israelites wrestling with Giant Snakes**

whenever the human figure was the focus of his attention. Particularly, in his early years in Italy, the confrontation with Michelangelo's power and vitality must have galvanized Rubens's own imagination. A drawing like the present one gives an idea of Rubens's effort to come to grips with Michelangelo's ideas concerning the human figure in action and to transform them into a vocabulary of his own.

C.M.

Fig 21-1 Michelangelo Buonarroti *The Brazen Serpent*. Sistine Chapel, Vatican, Rome

1   Held 1959, 58–60.
2   I am indebted to Professor Haverkamp-Begemann for his thoughts concerning this complicated problem.
3   London 1977, no. 16.
4   Fubini and Held 1964, 125, pls. 2 and 3.

22 Studies of Women

Sir Peter Paul Rubens

Siegen 1577–Antwerp 1640

22 Studies of Women

From Titian's *Poesie*

Black and red chalk, heightened with white; lower right corner
   restored
   448 × 286 mm

Fig 22-1 Titian *Diana surprised by Actaeon*. Duke of Sutherland Collection,
on loan to the National Gallery of Scotland, Edinburgh

Provenance: P.H. Lankrink (L. 2090); N. Beets; Drey; Dr. Gollnow; Dr. A. Schrafl

Bibliography: Müchall-Viebrook 1926, 8, no. 4; Glück and Haberditzl 1928, no. 3; Held 1959, I, 123, under no. 64; Burchard and d'Hulst 1963, no. 158; Jaffé 1977, 33, pl. XVI; Held 1982, 306; Held 1986, 56, no. 175

Malibu, The J. Paul Getty Museum. Inv. no. 82.GB.140

The present drawing which dates from Rubens's visit to Spain in 1628 contains studies after three of Titian's *Poesie*, the series of mythological paintings commissioned by Philip II in the 1550s.[1] At the bottom of the sheet is the head of Venus from the painting of *Venus and Adonis* in Madrid, at the top and centre are a female nude and the head of Diana taken from *Diana surprised by Actaeon* (Fig. 22–1). The heads at the right and upper left are from *The Discovery of the Shame of Callisto* (Fig. 22–2). These paintings, the latter two of which are now in Edinburgh, were still together in the Alcázar in Madrid in 1628.

Rubens sketched the head of Diana at the centre of the sheet in black and red chalk with white highlights, *aux trois crayons*. Like the unfinished head at the upper left, he first outlined it in black chalk, then added red to the eyelids, lips, nose, ear, and cheek to endow the flesh with colour and warmth. Other studies, such as the large head of Venus at the bottom, he sketched entirely in red chalk. Rubens chose rough textured paper resembling that used by Titian and other Venetian artists. This may have been a deliberate gesture on his part or he may have used it simply to further soften the chalk lines. In conjunction with the warm glow of the red chalk, it creates a granular effect suggesting light and atmosphere throughout. In style and execution this drawing pre-dates the head studies in Vienna for the *Ildefonso Altar* of 1630–32, in which red and black chalks are worked into each other with great sensitivity.[2]

This sheet of studies reflects the impact on Rubens of a most decisive experience in 1628, his renewed encounter with the art of the mature Titian in the Spanish royal collection. While Titian's paintings apparently meant comparatively little to Rubens at the time of his first visit to Madrid in 1603,[3] his art now became a revelation to the painter whose own artistic development after about 1620 had tended toward greater colouristic refinement and warmth. According to Velázquez's father-in-law, Pacheco, he copied every Titian in the collection of Philip IV.[4] From the 1640 inventory of Rubens's estate, we know that he painted replicas of all four *Poesie* for his own collection.[5] Like other artists (Cat. no. 54), Rubens faithfully copied works he desired but could not acquire.

Rubens probably made the present studies independently of the painted copies. From the *Poesie* he selected details as interpreted by a kindred spirit which he had long favoured in his own work – a nude woman bending forward, the tilted head of one young woman and heads of others seen from various becoming angles. In the process, Rubens endowed some of these details with his own ideal of feminine beauty. In spite of his sympathy for Titian's motifs and his indomitable urge to bestow the drawing with his own imprint, Rubens arranged the forms on the sheet as in the study sheets from his youth (Cat. no. 16). He continued the tradition even to the point of selecting motifs similar in type, in this case, the elegant feminine hair-do embellished with pearls and jewellery.

Shortly afterwards, about 1630, Rubens used the head below at the right for one of the nymphs in *The Bath of Diana* in Rotterdam.[6]

C.F.

1   Wethey 1975, 78–84, nos. 9, 10, 40, pls. 69, 84, 142.
2   Albertina, Vienna 1977, nos. 49, 50, 51.
3   In his youth, sometime before 1600, Rubens made a free copy after the group of Callisto held by her companions in Titian's *Discovery of the Shame of Callisto* from an engraving after Titian by Cornelis Cort (Burchard and d'Hulst 1963, no. 49; for the engraving by Cort, see Bierens de Haan 1948, no. 157, and Wethey 1975, fig. 216). A second drawing of Callisto with two nymphs after Cort's engraving which was published by Jaffé as an early copy by Rubens after Titian (Jaffé 1971, 41–46, fig. 2).
4   Pacheco [1649] 1956, 153.
5   Denucé 1932, 71. Two of Rubens's painted copies after the *Poesie* are known: *The Rape of Europa* in Boston and *The Discovery of the Shame of Callisto* in a private collection in England. See Jaffé 1977, 33–34, pl. 70. Contrary to general opinion, Jaffé does not believe that these copies were actually made in Spain, but rather after Rubens's return to Antwerp. Rubens's collection, including his copies after Titian and other artists, has now been studied extensively by Muller 1977 (book forthcoming).
6   Burchard and d'Hulst 1963, under no. 159. This painting forms the right half of a *Diana and Actaeon*, half of which is lost. The whole composition is known through an engraving by P. Spruyt of 1787.

Fig 22-2 Titian *The Discovery of the Shame of Callisto*. Duke of Sutherland
Collection, on loan to the National Gallery of Scotland, Edinburgh

23 Dormition of the Virgin

Benedetto Veli

Florence 1564–1639

23 Dormition of the Virgin
After a woodcut by Albrecht Dürer

Pen and brown ink over black chalk; laid down
   246 × 180 mm
Annotated lower left in pen: *di Benedetto Veli*
Bibliography: Thiem 1977, 307

Florence, Gabinetto dei Disegni e Stampe degli Uffizi. Inv. no. 7310F

Fig 23-1 Albrecht Dürer *The Death of the Virgin*. Rijksprentenkabinet, Amsterdam

Ever since del Sarto and Pontormo set the example, prints by Albrecht Dürer have served as compositional sources for Florentine painters. Benedetto Veli's drawing of *The Death of the Virgin* typifies the use Florentines made of the Northern artist's works. Possibly sketched in 1608 when Veli was commissioned to make an altarpiece, now lost, on this theme,[1] the drawing derives its compositional structure from Dürer's woodcut of this scene from the series *Life of the Virgin* (B. 93, Fig. 23–1). Veli, however, changed his model by narrowing the format and enlarging the number and scale of the figures. Whereas Dürer showed only the twelve Apostles set in a spacious room, Veli, in accordance with late Florentine mannerist taste, crowded his design with additional figures of ample volume. Moreover, Veli altered the narrative. Dürer's print includes St. John the Evangelist placing the taper in the Virgin's hands. In Veli's drawing, St. Peter holds the candle and has not yet presented it to the Virgin Mary.

Veli may have made this drawing at a fairly advanced stage of design since all the major components of the scene seem to have already been defined. The changes made in the course of drawing are minor, the inclination of heads of men in the foreground, for instance. By retaining the structure of a Dürer print while changing the subject, Veli partook of a Florentine tradition that began with such works as Pontormo's altarpiece for S. Michele in Visdomini.

A.B.

---

1   Thiem 1977, 307.

Herman Saftleven

Rotterdam 1609–Utrecht 1685

24 City View with Topographical Elements in the City of Prague
A pasticcio of motifs from Roelandt Savery

Black chalk, pen and black ink, and grey wash
348 × 382 mm
Provenance: Strölin; C. Hofstede de Groot
Bibliography: Bolten 1967, no. 95, pl. 219 (with further references); Bolten 1970, 11 and 14, pl. 4; Schulz 1982, no. 1033, pl. 74
Exhibitions: Previous to 1968 listed in Bolten 1967, no. 95; Padua-Florence-Venice 1968, no. 45

Groningen, Groninger Museum. Inv. no. 1931–227

Saftleven in this drawing created an imaginery view of Prague which strongly evokes the style of Roelandt Savery.[1] He probably copied this view by combining topographical elements found in Savery's works. His use of the shadowed foreground building to flank the central view of the city in the middle distance is reminiscent of some of Savery's drawings such as *House on the East Bank of the Vltava in Prague* (Fig. 24–1). Saftleven also imitated Savery's fine pen outlines and use of wash to convey the irregularities of the ageing architecture. He made at least four other drawings in Savery's style.[2]

As Schultz suggests, Saftleven upon his arrival in Utrecht in 1632 probably acquainted himself with the work of Savery who lived in the same city from 1619 to 1639. He could also have been introduced to Savery's drawings by Allaert van Everdingen, a former student of Savery's.[3] The impact of Savery is not only felt in the artist's early work, however. Even Saftleven's late mountain landscapes, in paintings as well as drawings, reflect the impetus of his admired predecessor, as do his studies of figures.

N.O.

Fig 24-1 Roelandt Savery *House on the East Bank of Vltava in Prague*. Staatliche Museen Preussischer Kulturbesitz, Kupferstichkabinett, Berlin

1   This drawing, once thought to have been by Savery himself as well as by Esaias van de Velde was attributed by Lugt and Frerichs to Saftleven (Bolten 1967, 118).
2   One, in the Städelsches Kunstinstitut, Frankfurt, inv. no. 936, also represents buildings. The other drawings imitate Savery's rocky, mountain landscapes: Kupferstichkabinett, Berlin, inv. no. 13833 (destroyed World War II); Hessisches Landesmuseum, Graphische Sammlung, Darmstadt, inv. no. AE-787; National Gallery Printroom, Edinburgh, inv. no. RSA-52.
3   Schulz 1982, 59.

24 **City View with Topographical Elements of the City of Prague**

25 Portrait of Ariosto

Theodoor Matham

Haarlem 1605/06–Amsterdam 1676

25 Portrait of Ariosto
After Titian

Black chalk over pencil, grey wash, red chalk, heightened with
   white (now oxidized)
278 × 190 mm (image: 183 × 147 mm)
Signed in pencil at upper left: *Theod. Matham del.*; inscribed,
   lower centre: *Titianus. V.P.* and lower right: *Ariosto poet*;
   below the drawing, a pencil sketch of a painting of the
   Madonna presenting Christ to Cardinal Richelieu(?)

Braunschweig, Herzog Anton Ulrich-Museum. Inv. no. Z 1305

From 1639 to 1641, Titian's so-called *Portrait of Ariosto*, the
Renaissance poet (National Gallery, London) and Raphael's
portrait of the courtier, *Baldassare Castiglione* (Musée du Louvre,
Paris), were in the collection of Alphonso Lopez, art dealer,
jeweller, and agent in The Netherlands for Cardinal Richelieu.[1]
Thus, for a brief period, the artistic community in Amsterdam
was afforded the opportunity to study these two seminal images
of Renaissance artistic personalities.[2] Matham, who was probably in Amsterdam by the late 1630s,[3] carefully interpreted
Titian's stately portrait (Fig. 25–1). He emphasized the sense
of movement and spontaneity conveyed by the tilted head, open
expression, and pronounced billowing of the ample sleeve. More
elaborately and carefully drawn than many of his portraits,
Matham's *Ariosto*, is also inscribed for documentation with his
signature on the work, the reproduction of Titian's name in bold-
face on the parapet, and at bottom right, the purported title
'Ariosto poet'.

In the margin of the drawing, Matham added a quick sketch,
probably of a painting, representing the Virgin Mary with the
Christ child, a donor, and a naked figure (a Saint?; Saint
Roch?). Since the painting probably belonged to Lopez, one is
inclined to think of Cardinal Richelieu as the donor, but evidence is lacking for the identification of the subject, as well as
the painter.

Roughly contemporary with Matham's drawing is the print
by Reinier van Persyn (Fig. 25–2). Its inscription indicates that
Persyn engraved it from a drawing by Joachim von Sandrart,
who also published it.[4] Presumably, the drawing by Sandrart
in Paris (Fig. 25–3) was Persyn's model. His print, however, differs from the drawing in Paris in several respects and shares some
features with the drawing by Matham. This raises the possibility
that Persyn worked from another drawing by Sandrart after the
one by Matham, particularly since Matham is known to have
worked for Sandrart in Rome in the 1630s.

   L.K.

Fig 25-1 Titian *Portrait of a Gentleman in Blue*. Reproduced courtesy of the
Trustees of the National Gallery, London

1   Gould 1975, 280–282, no. 1944. For Lopez, see Lugt 1936 (II), 114;
Stechow 1942; Bloch 1946.
2   Titian's painting was in Amsterdam from about 1639 to 1641, when
it was auctioned at Paris and possibly sold to Anthony van Dyck. See Gould
1975 for further history of the painting. The location of the painting in the
Lopez Collection is based on the evidence of the inscription on Persyn's print,
see below note 4.
3   M.D. Henkel wrote the most detailed biography of Theodoor, son of
the Haarlem printmaker Jacob Matham, in *Thieme-Becker*, 1930. As a reproductive printmaker, he engraved the works of artists such as Gerard Hon-
thorst and Cornelius Cort. After an apprenticeship in Rome with Sandrart
during the 1630s, he concentrated on engraving portraits and topographical
views. Matham is mentioned as being in Haarlem in 1641.
4   Hollstein XVII, no. 35. The inscription on the print reads: *Reg. Persinius
sculps./Joachimus Sandrart del. et excud. Amsterd: E Titiani prototypo in aedibus
Alph. Lopez* (with eight lines of text following). Sandrart 1675 (ed. Peltzer
[1925] 1975, 248) mentions this print in his discussion of Persyn.

Fig 25-2 Reinier van Persyn *Portrait of Ariosto*, after Titian.
Rijksprentenkabinet, Amsterdam

Fig 25-3 Joachim von Sandrart *Portrait of Ariosto*, after Titian. Fondation
Custodia (coll. F. Lugt), Institut Neerlandais, Paris

Nicolaes Berchem

Haarlem 1620–Amsterdam 1683

26 Figures from the Calling of St. Matthew
After Moeyaert

Black and white chalk on blue paper
198 × 264 mm
Annotated with pen and brown ink at lower left: *Berchem/après son Maître Moeyaert*
Provenance: P. Sylvester; Egmont
Bibliography: Haverkamp-Begemann and Logan 1970, I, no. 341

New Haven, Yale University Art Gallery, Library Transfer. Inv. no. 1961.64.77

Berchem carefully copied this group in the middle distance of Moeyaert's *Calling of St. Matthew* (1639), now in the Herzog Anton Ulrich-Museum in Braunschweig (Fig. 26–1).[1] As Haverkamp-Begemann and Logan have pointed out, this drawing helps to substantiate the assertion of Arnold Houbraken, the early seventeenth-century biographer of Netherlandish artists, that Berchem had trained with the renowned Amsterdam artist.[2] As it barely anticipates Berchem's mature style, the drawing probably predates his journey to Rome in 1643/44. Only the quickly-sketched figure to the right suggests the vibrant and lively manner which Berchem would later apply to subjects drawn from peasant life and history.[3]

C.M.

1 Bernt 1980, II, no. 831.
2 Haverkamp-Begemann and Logan 1970, I, no. 341.
3 *Ibid.*; see also Hoogewerff 1931, 84–87.

26 **Figures from the Calling of St. Matthew**

Fig 26-1 Moyaert *Calling of St. Matthew*. Herzog Anton Ulrich-Museum,
Braunschweig

27 St. Michael overcoming the Devil

Alessandro Algardi

Bologna 1598–Rome 1654

27 St. Michael overcoming the Devil
After Guido Reni's painting

Red chalk
228 × 147 mm
Bibliography: Budde 1930, 83, no. 604, pl. 93; Montagu 1985,
I, 200 and n. 62, 203, fig. 237, II, 480, no. 21

Düsseldorf, Kunstmuseum Düsseldorf. Inv. no. FP. 1521

This drawing was recently identified as a copy by Algardi of
Guido Reni's altarpiece of 1635 (Fig. 27–1);[1] previously, it was
believed to be a preliminary study for the painting by Reni himself.[2] Jennifer Montagu accepts the attribution to Algardi in her
recent monograph on the sculptor and, moreover, specifies that
he drew the copy c. 1647 when planning a small bronze of the
same theme.[3]

If we accept this attribution, it is clear that Algardi primarily
changed the pose of the Archangel. In the drawing, St. Michael
stands more erect than he does in the painting. The raised position of the head and left arm in the copy furthers the appearance
of stability. Rather than pose, the draughtsman used line and
shifts in tone to create a sense of motion, for instance, in the impli-
cit interplay of the outlines of the angel's left wing, right side
and drapery.

Montagu believes the frontal composition and the fall of the
drapery were the major elements of the painting which Algardi
incorporated in his bronze.[4] The straightened pose of the angel
in the drawing may foreshadow some of the changes the sculptor
was to bring to his statuette.

Widely copied in the seventeenth century,[5] Reni's altarpiece
in turn refers to another painting: Raphael's *St. Michael* painted
for François Ier in 1518. Consequently, this drawing reflects both
why Reni was regarded a new Raphael, and why Algardi was
called a 'new Guido in marble'.[6]

A.B.

Fig 27-1 Guido Reni *St. Michael overcoming the Devil*. Santa Maria della
Concezione, Rome

1　According to Montagu 1985, I, 200 n. 62, the new attribution was made
by Catherine Johnston.
2　The drawing is still catalogued by the Kunstmuseum as by Guido Reni;
see Budde 1930, 83.
3　Montagu 1985, I, 200.
4　*Ibid.*
5　Pepper 1984, 272, no. 154 provides a list of seventeenth-century copies.
6　Malvasia, as quoted by Montagu 1985, I, 200.

28 **Figures from the 'Parnassus'**

Nicolas Poussin

Les Andelys 1594–Rome 1665

28 Figures from the 'Parnassus'
After Raphael's fresco

Brush over preliminary drawing in pen, both with brown ink
    on beige paper
162 × 333 mm
Provenance: H. de Marignane (L. 1872); Sale, N. Rauch,
    Geneva, 7–11 June 1960, no. 311, repr.
Bibliography: Friedländer and Blunt 1974, V, 43; Blunt 1974,
    239–240, 246 n. 7, pl. 3; Blunt 1979, 146–147, fig. 165
Exhibitions: New York 1973 (II), no. 88; Paris 1983/84,
    no. 197; Cambridge 1985, no. 103; Vienna 1986, no. 74;
    Munich 1986, no. 74; Madrid 1986/87, no. 88; London
    1987, no. 73

New York, The Ian Woodner Family Collection, Inc. Inv.
    no. WCII-88

In this drawing, Poussin studied the central group of figures of
Raphael's *Parnassus* (Fig. 28–1), the fresco in the Stanza della
Segnatura in the Vatican (1510/11). He eliminated their landscape setting of rocky terrain and slender trees and reduced the
multitude of details to the essential features of the group. He
did so by the restrictive yet demanding means of flat brown
washes contrasting with the untouched paper, and a few
penlines. He thus substituted an abstract simplicity for Raphael's
formal and narrative complexity, thereby emphasizing his classical clarity. Poussin included one of the muses outside and to the
right of this group in the upper left corner of the sheet above
the seated scribe and left-out the head of the poet Statius to the
right of Homer.[1]

In the 1678 inventory of Poussin's studio, almost half of the
artist's own drawings were bound in a volume described as 'a
book of drawings made by monsieur Poussin from the Antique,
after Raphael, Giulio Romano and others, for his own use . . .'.[2]
Blunt suggested that Poussin may have wanted these drawings
to eventually be engraved in order for future generations of
artists to understand his conception of the classical tradition.[3]
Stylistically, this drawing cannot be grouped with these boldly
outlined drawings, rather it is comparable to his studies for the
second series of the *Sacraments* (*c.* 1644/45).[4] Poussin's intentions
in this case are more difficult to reconstruct. Yet, Poussin may
also have sought to profess his classical ideals in the present drawing in which he reduces the *Parnassus* to what seemed to him
the essentials.

Poussin's painted works make obvious his admiration for
Raphael. Yet this admiration is not reflected in his drawings
since in addition to the copy exhibited only one other drawing
by Poussin after Raphael, a study of details, is known.

    J.C.

Fig 28-1 Raphael *Parnassus*, (detail). Stanza della Segnatura, Vatican,
Rome

---

1   Blunt 1974, 239–240 and Cuzin in Paris 1983/84, no. 197. Although
the head of Statius is also omitted in Marcantonio Raimondi's engraving
after the fresco, Poussin did not make his drawing from the print.
2   Blunt 1979, 127.
3   Blunt 1979, 139.
4   Friedländer and Blunt 1939, I, nos. 78, 87–89, 95–96. Schab in New
York 1973 (II) proposed a date in the 1640s. This dating was accepted by
Miller in Vienna 1986 and Miller and Turner in London 1987. Blunt had
placed this drawing earlier and had suggested that Poussin used it as a point
of departure for his *Parnassus* (Prado); Blunt 1966, no. 129 and Blunt 1979,
240 and 246 n. 7.
5   Blunt 1979, 146, noted only one other direct copy after Raphael, a
'rough note' after two heads in the *Healing of the Lame Man*.

Claude Lorrain

Champagne 1600–Rome 1684

29 Harbour Scene
After Paul Bril

Chalk, pen and brown wash
　195 × 262 mm
Inscribed on *verso*: *Claudio fecit/in V.R.*
Provenance: Duke of Devonshire

Fig 29-1 Paul Bril *Harbour Scene*. Musées Royaux des Beaux-Arts, Brussels

Bibliography: Röthlisberger 1959, 46 and 49 n. 15; Röth-
　lisberger 1961, no. 30, fig. 76; Röthlisberger 1968, no. 191;
　Kitson 1978, no. 30

London, Trustees of the British Museum. Inv. no. 1957-12-14-36

This drawing is a remarkable link between the harbour scene
as it was established by the Flemish landscapists working in Italy
in the first quarter of the seventeenth century and Claude Lorraine's own momentous redefinition of the subject. In it, he seems
to have copied with variations a painting by one of the foremost
members of the group, Paul Bril, which is known in four versions.[1] The one now in Brussels (Fig. 29–1) is closest to Claude's
drawing and may have been the version Bril painted for G.B.
Crescenzi, himself a patron of Claude in Rome.[2]

　The drawing is numbered *30* on the *verso* and forms part of
the *Liber Veritatis*, the volume of drawings by Claude after his
own finished paintings. But there is neither a corresponding
painting nor an indication on the *verso* of the patron and city
for which the original work would have been made as Claude
noted on most of the other two hundred drawings in the volume.[3]

29 **Harbour Scene**

Regardless of whether Claude drew from Bril's example directly or whether he copied his own painting based on Bril's, the present drawing is so close in composition to Bril's *Harbour Scene* that Claude must have worked from one of the four known versions or, since no one closer than Fig. 29–1 is known, from one now lost. Another drawing from the *Liber Veritatis* (LV 9) which corresponds to a painting in Paris is also based on the work of an admired predecessor, Herman van Swanevelt's painting of the *Campo Vaccino*.[4]

The composition of the drawing is old-fashioned for Claude.

Indeed, the diagonal framework, the contrasting planes, the high viewpoint, and dramatic lighting depend directly on Bril's example. Claude, however, introduced a more unified and coherent spatial effect by lowering the horizon line and subordinating all elements to the group of ships in the right foreground. This strong *repoussoir* with a balance between the main points of emphasis would become a hallmark of his later work, as in his *Seaport with the Embarkation of Ulysses* (Musée du Louvre).[5]

C.M.

1   For reproductions of these four paintings (in Musées Royaux des Beaux-Arts, Brussels; Uffizi, Florence; Palazzo Borghese, Rome; and Ambrosiana, Milan), see Röthlisberger 1961, figs. 429–432.
2   In 1610, Cardinal Borromeo commissioned the Milan version from Bril, as a copy of a work which the artist was executing for Giovanni Battista Crescenzi who later commissioned a fresco cycle from Claude (Röthlisberger 1959, 46, and 49 n. 15). The Milan version was also engraved.
3   Although Kitson 1978, no. 30 does not concur, Röthlisberger 1968, no. 191 believes this drawing is a direct copy of a composition by Bril.
4   Kitson 1978, no. 9.
5   Röthlisberger 1961, fig. 177.

Rembrandt Harmensz. van Rijn

Leiden 1606–Amsterdam 1669

30 Susanna and the Two Elders
After Pieter Lastman

Red chalk
235 × 364 mm
Signed at lower right: *Rf.*; On the *verso*, Rembrandt wrote a note about the sale of paintings, among them works by his pupils Bol and Leendert van Beyeren
Provenance: Andreossy; Gigoux; Von Beckerath (bequeathed in 1902)
Bibliography: Hofstede de Groot 1906, no. 45 [not as after Lastman]; Bode 1908, fig. 35, 62; Freise 1911, 253; Kauffmann 1924 (II), 73; Müller 1929, 55; Benesch 1954, II, no. 448 (with further references); Haak 1969, 42; Stechow 1969, 148–149, 153, fig. 1; Strauss et al. 1979, 594–595, fig. 3
Exhibition: Berlin 1930, no. 225

Berlin, Staatliche Museen Preussischer Kulturbesitz, Kupferstichkabinett. Inv. no. KdZ 5296

In this work Rembrandt reinterpreted the painting his teacher Pieter Lastman had made in 1614 (Fig. 30–1). He employed red chalk to swiftly transcribe the entire scene, as he did in other drawings after Lastman.[1] Here, as in others, he reformulated Lastman's dramatic interpretation of a biblical narrative set against an elaborate landscape.

Rembrandt chose to reassess Lastman's historical narratives in the mid-1630s, about twelve years after leaving the elder's studio. All his copies after Lastman are from works by the master that predate his apprenticeship. Although it has been suggested that Lastman's death and the subsequent auction of his studio in 1633 may have triggered Rembrandt's desire to study these works,[2] his interest in Lastman's historical painting was of long duration and remained strong throughout his career.

At the time when Rembrandt executed this work (in or about 1635), he generally favoured pen and ink for drawing. Rembrandt may have chosen red chalk for this and other copies of paintings (Cat. no. 31) to avoid the linearity of the pen in favour of the broader, painterly and colourful effect of this medium.

Although Rembrandt's source is clearly recognizable, he did make subtle, but significant changes in his interpretation of this dramatic tale. In keeping with his concern for the psychological dimension of his characters, Rembrandt tried to give the figure of Susanna the appropriate expression, drawing her several times. In contrast to Lastman's figures, who communicate with wide, stage-like gestures, Rembrandt's bather, tensely perched on the stone fountain expresses her anger and worry with her arched back and eyes riveted upon the intruders. Where Lastman has all three of his characters participate in the histrionic scene, Rembrandt creates a foil for the emotionally charged Susanna by incorporating more fully the elders into the idyllic landscape background.

Rembrandt returned to the theme of Susanna at various moments over the next decades. These works culminate in the painting of 1647 in Berlin (Fig. 30–2) which still echoes Last-

Fig 30-1 Pieter Lastman *Susanna and the Two Elders*. Staatliche Museen
Preussischer Kulturbesitz, Gemäldegalerie, Berlin

man's painting.[3] In the relationship between the figures in this
painting, Rembrandt developed further the changes he initiated
in the drawing.

    L.K.

1   Rembrandt also copied Lastman's *Bathsheba*, *Diana and Acteon*, *The Ston-
ing of St. Stephen* (an etching), *The Raising of the Cross*, and other works. For
the drawings after Lastman, see Müller 1929, 55–56 and Freise 1911, 253.
2   Bode 1908, 58.
3   See Kauffmann 1924 (II), 73.

30 Susanna and the Two Elders

Fig 30-2 Rembrandt Harmensz. van Rijn *Susanna and the Two Elders*.
Staatliche Museen Preussischer Kulturbesitz, Gemäldegalerie, Berlin

Rembrandt Harmensz. van Rijn

Leiden 1606–Amsterdam 1669

31 The Last Supper
After Leonardo da Vinci's fresco

Red chalks

365 × 475 mm

Signed lower right: *Rembrant f.*; inscribed at bottom centre: *Wt*[. . .]*d*[. . .]

Provenance: J. Friedrich August II of Saxony

Bibliography: Lippmann 1888–1901, I, no. 99; Michel 1893, 406; Hofstede de Groot 1894, 178; Hofstede de Groot 1906, 71–72, no. 297; Neumann 1918, 106–108, fig. 34; Valentiner 1925, 1934, II, 195, pl. 623B, 409, no. 623; Weisbach 1926, 197–199, fig. 46; Hell 1930, 111, no. 1; Lugt 1931, 62 under no. 1369; Hind 1932, 61, pl. XXXIX; van Rijckevorsel 1932, 236–237, fig. 293; Benesch 1935, 21; van Regteren Altena 1948/49, 14; Lugt 1952, 40–41; Benesch 1954, II, no. 443, fig. 500; Maison 1966, 105, pl. 125; van de Waal [1956] 1974, 256–257, fig. 13; Gantner 1962, 179–184, fig. 4; White 1962, 12–13; Rotermund 1963, 261, fig. 216; Gantner 1964, 36–40, fig. 12; Slive 1965, I, no. 134, no. 19; Heydenreich 1974, 71; Hyatt Mayor 1978/79, 29, fig. 23; Slatkes 1983, 42, fig. 20; Wheelock in Washington 1983/84, no. 15; Schatborn 1985, 186, n. 5 under no. 87

Exhibitions: Paris 1957, no. 122; Washington etc. 1958/59, no. 60; Cincinnati 1959, no. 268; New York–Cambridge 1960, no. 9; Chicago-Minneapolis-Detroit 1969/70, no. 100; Washington 1977, no. 33; New York 1979 (II), no. 23; Washington 1983/84, no. 15

New York, The Metropolitan Museum of Art, Robert Lehman Collection 1975. Inv. no. 1975.1.794

This drawing represents not only Rembrandt's public statement of his admiration for Leonardo's *Last Supper*, but is also a testimony to his desire to nurture his own creative power under the impetus of Leonardo's achievement. It is one of the most impressive interpretations, if not *the* most impressive one, by a seminal artist of a fundamental work by another. Rembrandt copied an engraving after Leonardo's *Last Supper* (Fig. 31–1) initially in hard red chalk, adhering closely to the original in certain areas, deviating from it in others.[1] He then reworked the entire drawing with softer red chalk, rearranging the figures within their groupings, rethinking every single disciple's function, gesture and expression. Rembrandt altered the figure of Christ to sit straight with His head close to His body and so charged Him with an expressiveness absent from Leonardo's example. He made Judas (fourth from left) recoil and thus infused his form with the psychological tension appropriate to his role in this drama.[2]

Rembrandt intensified not only each figure but also the scene as a whole. He pushed the table and the figures towards the viewer by eliminating the large hall that, in Leonardo's *cenacolo* and the print after it, diminishes the size of the figures and pulls them back into its space.[3] With his usual abhorrence of symmetry, Rembrandt placed Christ to the left of centre, and emphatically eliminated Leonardo's classical balance by putting

31 The Last Supper

a canopy obliquely above Christ rather than directly above Him. In so doing he also suggested a different position for the viewer. In Leonardo's *Last Supper*, the viewer is presumed to stand directly before the centre of the table, in Rembrandt's to the left of centre, since in the pictorial space the canopy is situated centrally above Christ.

The bold, second stage of the drawing is often dated to the 1650s, mainly because the canopy is repeated in several of Rembrandt's paintings from this time; however, it is also thought to have been carried out shortly after the initial work.[4] This seems more likely, because the angular lines resemble those of Rembrandt's copies after Lastman from the mid-thirties, and because Rembrandt did not use red chalk, to our knowledge, much later than the mid-1630s.

Rembrandt interpreted Leonardo's *Last Supper* in two other drawings as well (London and Berlin),[5] working out some of the thoughts he formulated in this large, monumental recasting of the entire scene. His dialogue with Leonardo obviously was of great significance to him. He signed both the Lehman drawing and the one in Berlin, as if to assert that this was his own rendition of the famous *Last Supper*. Under the Lehman drawing he also wrote a few words of which only two or three letters can be made out now. The beginning of the inscription seems to read 'Wt', for 'From' or 'After'.

Rembrandt never could put Leonardo's *Last Supper* out of his mind when he wished to represent 'Christ and His Disciples' or scenes of one principal figure among others gathered around a table. His etchings and paintings of *Christ at Emmaus*, his late *Conspiracy of Claudius Civilis and the Batavians* are all dependent in part on impulses received from Leonardo's fresco.[6] Particularly strong, however, is the connection in his *Wedding Feast of Samson* of 1638 (Dresden, Fig. 31–2). The group of figures who attentively listen to the gesturing Samson clearly relates to the reworked group on the right side of the Lehman drawing.[7]

In this context, Rembrandt's early drawing, *Christ and His Disciples* (Teylers Museum, Haarlem)[8] should be mentioned. It is dated 1634 and differs markedly from the composition of Leonardo's fresco. Given the forceful impact of the *Last Supper* on Rembrandt, one may conclude that the drawing in Haarlem represents Rembrandt's effort to solve the problems of representing Christ and his disciples before he knew the work of his Italian predecessor.

E.H.-B.

1   Schatborn's opinion (1985, 186) that the drawing 'may be the work of a student which was corrected by Rembrandt' fails to take into consideration the fundamental differences from the original print already introduced in the first stage of this drawing. The background space, to mention one salient deviation, is already transformed into a wall immediately behind the figures. The figure of Christ in the first red chalk version is indeed still very similar to the one in the print, but its visibility should not obscure the innovative nature of other sections of this first sketch.
2   Rembrandt's changes have been analysed frequently, notably by Gantner 1964, and also, particularly perceptively in the case of Judas, by Clark 1966, 54.
3   The function of a wall behind the figures as a means to propel them towards the viewer was discussed à propos of Rembrandt and as a Caravagesque characteristic by van de Waal [1969] 1974, 13–27.
4   The first opinion was represented in, a.o., Neumann 1918, 106–108; Chicago 1969, no. 100; Washington 1977, no. 33; the later in a.o., Benesch 1935, 21; Benesch 1954, II, no. 443; Slive 1965, I, no. 100; Clark 1966, 54; Washington 1983/84, no. 15.
5   Benesch 1954, II, nos. 444 and 445; Gantner 1964, 35–51.

Fig 31-1 Giovanni Pietro da Birago after Leonardo *Last Supper with the Spaniel*. Staatliche Museen Preussischer Kulturbesitz, Kupferstichkabinett, Berlin

6   Gantner 1964, even if not all his interpretations can be accepted, discusses all of Rembrandt's works related in one way or the other to Leonardo's *Last Supper*.

7   This provides an additional *terminus ante quem* for the Lehman drawing. Slatkes 1983, 43–51, has suggested that the similarity between the compositions of the Lehman drawing and the Dresden painting was not only determined by the typological relationship between their subjects but also by theoretical implications. Slatkes suggests that Rembrandt may have intentionally used both the composition of Leonardo's *Last Supper* and the counting gesture described by Leonardo in his *Trattato della Pittura* as an open challenge to the classical ideals championed by Joachim von Sandrart and his circle who were living in Amsterdam at this time.

8   Benesch 1954, I, no. 89, fig. 97. If the drawing in Haarlem preceded the Lehman drawing, the latter can be dated to 1634 or 1635, since Rembrandt's drawing after Leonardo in Berlin (Benesch 1954, II, 445) dated 1635 in all likelihood followed the Lehman drawing.

Fig 31-2 Rembrandt Harmensz. van Rijn *Wedding Feast of Samson*.
Gemäldegalerie, Dresden

32 An English Woman

Rembrandt Harmensz. van Rijn

Leiden 1606–Amsterdam 1669

32 An English Woman
After Hans Holbein the Younger

Pen and brown ink
191 × 126 mm
Notations on *verso*
Bibliography: Van Regteren Altena 1967, 377
Exhibition: Oslo 1976, no. 41

Oslo, Nasjonalgalleriet. Inv. no. B 15589

This drawing, formerly attributed to the School of Rembrandt and recently recognized by van Regteren Altena as by Rembrandt himself, is a copy of a pen and watercolour drawing by Hans Holbein the Younger (Fig. 32–1) representing an English woman.[1] Rembrandt transcribed only the upper three-quarters of the figure and abbreviated many of the details – the tassels of the belt, for example, he rendered in a single sweep of the pen. Furthermore, he introduced a variety of linear rhythms which serve as a vibrant substitute for the colour of Holbein's work. The voluminous gown falls in heavy, disorderly folds and the transparent veil seems to respond to a spontaneous flurry of wind. Thereby, Rembrandt introduced a new sense of weight and motion to his model.

The same figure van Regteren Altena also recognized as a servant girl in another drawing by Rembrandt, *Lot and his Daughters*, in the British Museum (Fig. 32–2).[2] Except for the servant girl, Rembrandt based this drawing on an engraving of the same subject after Rubens, and so combined the unruly rhythms of the Flemish composition with the quiet poise of Holbein's figure. It has been dated *c.* 1650, postdating the present drawing by a decade, and is more complete, including the woman's longer skirt and sandaled feet. Thus Rembrandt must have had access to Holbein's drawing more than once. Possibly, the drawing by Holbein was included in one of two portfolios recorded in the 1656 inventory of Rembrandt's possessions containing drawings and prints 'by the principal masters of the whole world'.[3] From the numerous copies after Mughal miniatures (Cat. nos. 33 and 34), we know that Rembrandt had a keen interest in foreign costume and figure types and often used them for the biblical personages in his prints and paintings. Just as he associated a Mughal prince with a biblical personage in Cat. no. 34, he may initially have been drawn to Holbein's figure for her costume and type in view of possible adaptation in a narrative scene.

L.K.

Fig 32-1 Hans Holbein the Younger *A Young English Woman*. Ashmolean Museum, Oxford

1   Van Regteren Altena 1967, 377; Oslo 1976, no. 41. For the Holbein drawing, see Parker 1938, no. 298.
2   Benesch 1956, IV, no. A 36, fig. 1041 as doubtful. The drawing was accepted by Lugt 1933 under no. 1207, as from 1650, or somewhat later, and 1936 (I), under no. 246 as from *c.* 1652–55 and Rosenberg 1959, 116, as from the late 1650s. Both Lugt and Rosenberg recognized that the drawing was reworked by a later hand. Van Regteren Altena 1967, 378 as by Rembrandt.
3   Rembrandt's inventory is listed most recently in Strauss et al. 1979, 349 ff. The two volumes mentioned are listed under nos. 199 and 203.

Fig 32-2 Rembrandt Harmensz. van Rijn *Lot and his Daughters*. Trustees of
the British Museum, London

Rembrandt Harmensz. van Rijn

Leiden 1606–Amsterdam 1669

33 Two Indian Noblemen
After Mughal miniatures

Pen and brown ink, brown wash, with touches of red wash, and red and yellow chalk, on oriental paper
191 × 234 mm
Inscribed in pen and brown ink on *verso* at upper margin (illegible)
Provenance: J. Richardson, Sr. (L. 2184); C. Rogers (L. 624–26); J.J. Goll van Franckenstein the Younger [according to Hofstede de Groot]; Finch, Fifth Earl of Aylesford (L. 58); C. Fairfax Murray; J.P. Morgan (L. 1509)
Bibliography: Fairfax Murray 1905, I, no. 208; Hofstede de Groot 1906, no. 1087; Benesch 1957, V, no. 1203; Ettinghausen 1961, 6; Stechow 1971, 488, fig. 3; Lunsingh Scheurleer 1980, 28–29, fig. 16
Exhibitions: Paris 1908, no. 428; New York 1918, no. 29; Toronto 1951, no. 3; Chicago-Minneapolis-Detroit 1969/70, no. 107; New York 1979 (I), no. 76 (with further references)

New York, The Pierpont Morgan Library. Inv. no. I, 208

This drawing once belonged to an album of twenty-five Rembrandt drawings after Indian miniatures of the Mughal School, works which are contemporary with Rembrandt's oeuvre.[1] Since the two figures face each other, yet look in different directions, it is likely that Rembrandt has combined figures from two separate miniatures on a single sheet (Fig. 33–1, 33–2). Although the identities of these two courtiers have been established with some certainty, it is not clear whether Rembrandt would have known whom the figures portrayed.[2]

In this copy, he has used a fine precise pen for most of the lines, adding tone with washes, and accents with touches of red and yellow chalks to the costumes and accessories – shoes, robes, sword, and the falcon. His choice of media, support, and tools seems to have been governed by the wish to capture the delicacy and sensitivity of the original miniatures.

The precise sources and dates of Rembrandt's copies of Mughal miniatures still remain unclear. Glück (1933) first proposed that the drawings copied the miniatures which now line the walls of the Millionenzimmer at the Schönbrunn Palace in Vienna.[3] Recent research has provided no corroboration of earlier claims that Rembrandt studied, and perhaps even owned, such miniatures.[4] Although there is no solid evidence that Mughal miniatures were common in The Netherlands much before 1650, it is likely that examples of various quality were already available by that time. Rembrandt may have based his drawings on any number of miniatures on the art market in Amsterdam.[5]

Rembrandt's life-long interest in oriental figures originally was stimulated by the works of Adam Elsheimer and Pieter Lastman. Mughal-like figures appear in his prints, for instance, *The Three Crosses* (B. 78) and *La Petite Tombe* (B. 67), all of which date from the early 1650s.[6] This drawing, like Cat. no. 34 and others from the series, is drawn on 'Japan' paper, actually Indian

Figs 33-1, 33-2 Mughal School *Indian Nobleman*. Schönbrunn Palace,
Vienna

33 Two Indian Noblemen

Fig 33-3 Eugène Delacroix *Indian Nobleman*, after a Mughal miniature. Musée du Louvre, Cabinet des Dessins, Paris

paper, thin, with a wheat-coloured cast. Rembrandt also frequently printed etchings on such paper in the 1650s.[7] It is likely that these copies of Mughal miniatures date from the early to mid-1650s.

Later, in the nineteenth century, Eugène Delacroix followed Rembrandt's lead in copying Mughal miniatures (Fig. 33–3) in preparation for his canvas of middle eastern drama, *The Death of Sardanapalus* of 1827 (Musée du Louvre).[8] Delacroix, like Rembrandt, found several opportunities to draw on his precise studies of Mughal miniatures when creating freer interpretations of these exotic subjects.

Rembrandt's interpretation of Mughal miniatures is discussed further in the next entry.

L.K.

1   See Benesch 1957, V, no. 1187 for the history of this album. Lunsingh Scheurleer 1980 has pointed out that the miniatures copied by Rembrandt span a period from about 1610 to 1650, therefore suggesting that he studied such miniatures as contemporary art.

2   Lunsingh Scheurleer 1980, 28 and New York 1979. R. Ettinghausen (1961) established the identity of the elder figure on the right as Abd-al-Rahim, Khan-i-Khanan (1556–1626), a learned courtier during the reigns of both Akbar and Jahangir, successive Emperors of the Mughal realm. The younger figure on the left is probably Khan Alem, an ambassador in Jahangir's court to the Shah of Persia from 1615 to 1623. He was also keeper of the falcons at court, as indicated by the falcon he holds in this and in many other portraits.

3   Strzygowski 1923 and others have described the installation in Vienna.

4   Lunsingh Scheurleer 1980 points out that the Schönbrunn miniatures, which may in fact have belonged to a seventeenth-century Dutch collection, are badly overpainted, and are not the best examples of the types that appear in Rembrandt's drawings. He is not convinced that this was the group used by Rembrandt. He also notes that the miniatures first suggested by Sarre (1904, 1909) as Rembrandt's models are actually eighteenth-century copies of seventeenth-century images. For history of the miniatures, see Strzygowski 1923.

The possibility that Rembrandt owned a set of Mughal miniatures is traditionally linked to an entry in the 1656 inventory listing an album of 'curious miniatures'. His series of Mughal drawings have therefore been dated to the mid-1650s. However, Lunsingh Scheurleer 1980, 15, notes that if this entry did refer to Mughal miniatures, the album more likely would have been designated by one of the several terms commonly used in The Netherlands at the time, such as 'Mogolse', 'Suratse', or 'Oost-Indiaanse'. He doubts whether this inventory note proves Rembrandt owned albums of Mughal minatures.

5   See Lunsingh Scheurleer 1980. Also New York 1979, no. 75, points out that Rembrandt could have seen several versions proximate to the Schönbrunn miniatures in Amsterdam.

6   Suggested by Lunsingh Scheurleer 1980.

7   New York 1979, no. 75.

8   Rosenthal 1977.

Rembrandt Harmensz. van Rijn

Leiden 1606–Amsterdam 1669

34 Portrait of Shah Jahan
After Mughal miniature

Pen and brown ink and brown wash on oriental paper lightly
toned with brown wash
225 × 171 mm
Inscribed by Sir Gore Ouseley on *verso* of mount: *Portrait of Shah
Jahan Emperor of Hindustan* followed by words in Arabic, and
by another hand: *written by Sir Gore Ouseley*
Provenance: J. Richardson, Sr. (L. 2184); Sale, London, 22
January 1747, no. 70; Lord Brownlow; Sale, Sotheby's,
London, 29 June 1926, no. 25; W.R. Valentiner; Sale,
Amsterdam, 25 October 1926, no. XII; R. von Hirsch; Sale,
Sotheby's, New York, 20 June 1978, no. 38
Bibliography: Valentiner 1925, 34, no. 643; Benesch 1957, V,
no. 1193 (with further references); Clark 1966, 166–167;
Cleveland 1979, 3; Broos 1980, 210–211, fig. 1; Lunsingh
Scheurleer 1980, no. 18, 30–32; Broos in Amsterdam 1986,
76, fig. a; Bredius 1936, 1937, no. 631
Exhibition: Basel 1948, no. 29

Cleveland, The Cleveland Museum of Art, Purchase Leonard
C. Hanna Jr. Fund. Inv. no. CMA 78.38

This drawing originally belonged to the same album of Rembrandt sketches after Mughal miniatures as Cat. no. 33.[1] Here Rembrandt has depicted Shah Jahan (1592–1666), who inherited the Mughal Empire from his father Jahangir at its height, ruling from 1628 to 1658. An Emperor with deep religious convictions, Jahan revived Persian influence at court, and also displayed examples of western religious painting at his palace.[2] He built the Taj Mahal for his wife Mumtaz Mahal.

For this drawing Rembrandt apparently had access to a portrait of the young Jahan from around 1635 (Fig. 34–1).[3] The grand Mughal stands erect, his elegant and authoritative dignity expressed by his bearing, his fine costume, his long vertical sword, and his dainty fly swatter.[4] Carefully choosing his media and utensils, Rembrandt transposed his model into his personal idiom. He selected Indian paper and enhanced its warm and absorbant tonality by covering it with a light wash. Using a very fine pen, finer than he was accustomed to handling, he drew the figure and then barely indicated the material substance of the costume with a brush so dry as to produce only faint strokes. Finally, he boldly set off the figure with fully loaded, quickly applied brush strokes. If Rembrandt's model had a background, he omitted its details.[5]

With an historical awareness that was not burdened by geographical and chronological demands Rembrandt, like Delacroix later, could equate eastern rulers with biblical potentates and saints. Although this drawing has been referred to as a costume study,[6] Rembrandt may have associated the Shah with biblical personages. In several of his own works including *Manoah's Sacrifice* (Benesch 980) and *The Wrath of Ahasuerus* (Moscow, Bredius 631), Rembrandt has depicted holy men in oriental dress reminiscent, in a general sense, of Mughal princes.[7]

L.K.

34 Portrait of Shah Jahan

Fig 34-1 Mughal School *Shah Jahan*. Schönbrunn Palace, Vienna

1   See Cat. no. 33 for further references to this album of drawings.

2   See Stchoukine 1929, 51 ff.

3   Lunsingh Scheurleer 1980, 30–31 points out that images of Shah Jahan may be dated somewhat by the growth of his beard, which filled out considerably in his later years. See *idem*. fig. 20.

4   The Shah's dress reflects the fashion of the 1630s, the late Jahangir period (Lunsingh Scheurleer 1980, 30).

5   Frits Lugt (Paris 1986, nos. 33, 34, 36, 61) collected with an understandable eagerness Mughal drawings which being largely linear and with hardly any colour are distinct from Mughal miniatures. It is likely that Rembrandt, at least in some cases, copied such outline brush drawings rather than fully coloured miniatures.

6   Broos 1980, 211.

7   Slatkes 1983; the relationship between *Manoah's Sacrifice* and the orient was suggested by Clark 1966, 166–167.

35 **Isaac and Rebecca spied upon by Abimelech**

Rembrandt Harmensz. Van Rijn

Leiden 1606–Amsterdam 1669

35 Isaac and Rebecca spied upon by Abimelech
From an engraving after Raphael

Pen and brown ink, corrected with white (partly oxidized)
  145 × 185 mm
Provenance: L. Richter; E. Cichorius; O. Huldschinsky; W.R.
  Valentiner
Bibliography: Benesch 1957, V. no. 988; Clark 1966, 141–142,
  fig. 133; Tümpel 1969, pl. 45; Tümpel 1986, 351
Exhibitions: Rotterdam 1938, no. 327; Rotterdam–Amsterdam
  1956,no. 210;Chicago-Minneapolis-Detroit1969/70,no. 140
  (with further references)

Private Collection

In this drawing dating from his late years, Rembrandt reinterpreted a biblical love scene from a fresco of the Loggia in the
Vatican, once given to Raphael and now attributed to Giulio
Romano.[1] The scene (Genesis 26:8) depicts the moment when
the King of the Pharisees, Abimelech, realizes upon discovering
the couple embracing that Isaac and Rebecca are not brother
and sister, as Isaac had told him, but husband and wife.

Cornelius Müller first related Rembrandt's drawing to
Raphael's fresco,[2] and Tümpel proposed a print after the work,
the engraving by Sisto Badalocchio, as the direct source for the
drawing since its composition reverses the fresco's (Fig. 35–1).[3]

Rembrandt has included all three of the protagonists in his
drawing: the lovers and the king who furtively spies on them
from an upper balcony. He retained the triangular composition,
but altered the positions of the figures so as to highlight the emotional and psychological aspects of this well-known biblical tale.
By changing the background from a palace garden to a domestic
interior, Rembrandt was able to focus on the couple at very close
range, emphasizing their expressions and gestures. Clearly, he
was most interested in the tender interchange between Isaac and
Rebecca. After swiftly sketching the outlines of background and
figures, Rembrandt returned to the intertwined hands several
times. He drew the head of Isaac twice, the second time bringing
it closer to and so in more open admiration of Rebecca. Despite
Rembrandt's quick execution of the drawing, his corrections
indicate a thoughtful and purposeful reinterpretation of the
source.

This drawing is directly related to Rembrandt's painting
known as the *Jewish Bride* (Fig. 35–2). The connection between
the two, first noted by Valentiner,[4] has somewhat obscured
identification of the subject of both works. If they are directly
related, does the painting represent Isaac and Rebecca set in
contemporary times, in spite of the omission of King Abimelech?
Or, has Rembrandt painted portraits of a couple in biblical
dress? As van Schendel discovered through x-rays of the painting, originally Rembrandt had the woman seated on the man's
lap, which confirms the close relation between the painting and
the present drawing.[5] Regardless of the iconographical question,
we can see how in this drawing Rembrandt again amplifies the
human perspective of a religious or historical narrative.

Raphael's fresco attracted much attention throughout the

Fig 35-1 Sisto Badalocchio *Isaac and Rebecca spied upon by Abimelech*

Fig 35-2 Rembrandt Harmensz. van Rijn *Jewish Bride* Rijksmuseum,
Amsterdam

Renaissance and beyond. Many artists copied it, including the decorative ceramic painter Nicolò da Urbino, who worked at the Gonzaga court under Isabella d'Este,[6] and later, Eugène Delacroix.[7] His pen copy (Fig. 35–3), also made after an engraving, emphasizes in its own divergence from the source the literary bias of the Romantic era.

L.K.

Fig 35-3 Eugène Delacroix *Sheet of Studies with a Pair of Lovers*. Musée du Louvre, Cabinet des Dessins, Paris

1   Hartt 1981, I, 28–29.
2   Related by Müller verbally to Valentiner. See Valentiner 1925, 1934, no. 243.
3   Tümpel 1969, 163, from Badalocchio-Lanfranco, *Historia del Testamento Vecchio* . . . 1607, pl. 22. Tümpel mentions this as one of several engravings after the fresco. Rembrandt owned several portfolios of prints after works by Raphael and other Italian artists. See the 1656 inventory of his collection, reprinted in Fuchs 1969, 76–80, and elsewhere. For further discussion of Rembrandt's relation to Italian art, see the entry on his drawing of the *Last Supper*, Cat. no. 31.
4   Valentiner 1923, Tümpel 1969 summarizes the arguments on this question.
5   See Amsterdam 1969, 106, no. 22.
6   Mallet 1981, fig. 2.
7   Sérullaz 1984, II, no. 1429.

36 Large Farm with Figures

Lambert Doomer

Amsterdam 1624–1700

36 Large Farm with Figures
From a drawing by Roelandt Savery

Pen and brown ink, brown and grey washes over traces of preliminary drawing in pencil
355 × 512 mm
Provenance: Von Beckerath
Bibliography: Bock and Rosenberg 1930, 120; Schulz 1971, 256,
no. 5, 259, pl. 37; Schulz 1974, no. 252
Exhibition: Berlin 1974, no. 50, pl. 92

Berlin, Staatliche Museen Preussischer Kulturbesitz, Kupferstichkabinett. Inv. no. KdZ 12759

Only the left half of this *Large Farm with Figures* corresponds to
a drawing by Roelandt Savery (Fig. 36–1). The Savery-like
motif of the tree at the right in Doomer's drawing suggests that
his model was either cut down or consisted of two sheets, one
that still exists and a second one that continued the subject to
the right.[1] Doomer copied Savery's ageing farm buildings faithfully, but updated the scene by substituting staffage in contemporary costume for Savery's peasants in ragged dress.
Whereas the Savery drawing was typically drawn in chalk and
washes, Doomer translated Savery's lines to pen and washes
sharpening the depiction and introducing more intensified
lighting.[2]

In 1658 at one of the auctions of Rembrandt's possessions,
Lambert Doomer purchased an album of drawings of Tirolean
landscapes by Roelandt Savery. Rembrandt had purchased
these in 1639 at the auction of Savery's possessions upon his
death. As a pupil of Rembrandt, Doomer may have attached
special significance to this album as well as to the numerous other
art objects which he purchased at the auctions of Rembrandt's
possessions.[3] Although Doomer could have studied Savery's
drawings while he was in Rembrandt's studio from 1644 to 1645,
the style and mastery of his copies of Savery make a date around
1665, a decade after his purchase of the album, as Schulz suggests, more likely. Doomer may have copied his Savery drawings
before he sold part of them to Laurens van der Hem in that year.[4]

Doomer was one of the few Dutch artists of the seventeenth
century who documented foreign scenery during his travels, particularly along the Rhine and in France. His copies of Savery
demonstrate that his interest in the exotic comprised art as well
as reality.

    N.O.

Fig 36-1 Roelandt Savery *Large Farm with Figures*. Graphische Sammlung
Albertina, Vienna

1   Albertina, Vienna, inv. no. 9944. Schulz 1971, 256.
2   Schulz 1971, 256.
3   Schulz 1971, 258 n. 11.
4   Schulz 1971, 257.

37 Transfer of a Relic

Jan de Bisschop

Amsterdam 1628–The Hague 1671

37 Transfer of a Relic

From Lucas van Leyden

Pen, ink and wash
187 × 295 mm
Inscribed lower left: *L*; annotated on *verso*, upper left in brown
ink: *Bisschop/na Luijcas. v: Lijden.*
Provenance: J.J. Goll von Franckenstein (L. 2987); P. Blussé
van Zuidland en Velgersdijk; J. de Grez
Bibliography: Inventaire de Grez 1913, no. 311; van Gelder
1957, no. 3

Brussels, Musées Royaux des Beaux-Arts de Belgique. Inv. no. de
Grez 311

De Bisschop's rendering of a lost painting by Lucas van Leyden,
perhaps a predella to an altarpiece,[1] is undoubtedly quite close
to the original in style and detail. Copies by de Bisschop after
existing works by Lucas and other artists support this assump-
tion. Already in 1721 Houbraken praised the artist for his ability
to accurately imitate in drawing the painted styles of the artists
he copied.[2] The drawing therefore is a welcome and trustworthy
substitute for a lost original. The painting apparently represented the transfer of the relics of a saint that had miraculous
power to relieve the hardship of cripples and beggars.

The lawyer and artist Jan de Bisschop (who also called himself Episcopius) made many drawings after paintings, drawings,
and the antique. Some were engraved and these appeared either
individually[3] or were compiled into two books known as the
Icones and *Paradigmata*.[4] It is not known whether de Bisschop
intended to have this drawing engraved. In general, Lucas van
Leyden was held in high esteem by de Bisschop and his Dutch
contemporaries as the Dutch equivalent to Dürer. De Bisschop
himself may have had the opportunity to familiarize himself with
Lucas van Leyden's work as a law student in Leiden.

N.O.

1   Van Gelder 1957, 96. Van Gelder suggests this because of the crowded
horizontal composition which would be unusual for an altarpiece by Lucas
van Leyden.
2   Houbraken 1718–21, II, 167. See van Gelder 1971, 203–204 for criticism
of Houbraken's section on de Bisschop.
3   See for example de Bisschop's two prints after Breenbergh *Joseph dis-
tributing Corn* (H. 1) and *The Martyrdom of Saint Lawrence* (H. 3).
4   Van Gelder and Jost 1985.

38 Sheet of Studies

Antoine Watteau

Valenciennes 1684–Nogent-sur-Marne 1721

38 Sheet of Studies
From Rubens's Marie de Medici cycle

Trois crayons
    195 × 250 mm
Inscribed at the bottom centre: *Ant Watteau*
Provenance: Louise-Ulrica of Sweden; Count Steinbock; N. Barck (L. 1959); J.P. Heseltine; G. di Giuseppe
Bibliography: Guiraud 1913, no. 90; Parker and Mathey 1957, I, no. 266; Roland Michel 1984, 29, fig. 13
Exhibitions: Providence 1975, no. 37; Frankfurt 1982, no. Cb 12

Private Collection

The pair of figures at the top left Watteau copied from *The Debarkation of Marie de Medici at Marseilles*, the four heads he took from *The Coronation of Marie de Medici* (Fig. 38–1), both paintings from the Marie de Medici cycle which Rubens painted for the Palais du Luxembourg. It is likely that Watteau made these studies at the Luxembourg early in his career, between 1708 and 1711, while in the employment of the concierge of the King's Collection, Claude Audran III. Audran's assistants lived and worked in the Luxembourg Palace with free access to the works of art there.[1]

Watteau transformed details from the original paintings into delicate, introspective portrait studies. He softened Rubens's crisp contours and three-dimensional modelling by means of the *trois crayon* medium. The study of the two women at centre is very similar in spirit to his sensitive portrait studies from life.[2]

Rubens's paintings in the Palais du Luxembourg were copied all through the eighteenth and nineteenth centuries by French artists, among them Antoine Coypel, Delacroix, Géricault, and Cézanne, and thus exercised a lasting yet continually changing effect on French art.[3]
    P.V.

Fig 38-1 Sir Peter Paul Rubens *The Coronation of Marie de Medici*, (detail). Musée du Louvre, Paris

1   See Washington-Paris-Berlin 1984/85, 210 with further references.
2   See, for example, *Two Studies of a Child's Head and Four of a Woman* (Fogg Art Museum, Harvard University) and *Study Sheet with Nine Heads* (Musée du Petit Palais, Paris) reproduced in Washington-Paris-Berlin 1984/85, nos. 21 and 77.
3   See Thuillier and Foucart 1967, 132–153.

39 Head of a Woman

Antoine Watteau

Valenciennes 1684–Nogent-sur-Marne 1721

39 Head of a Woman
After Rubens

Red and black chalk with stumping on cream paper
310 × 228 mm
Annotated on the mount possibly in the hand of Mariette: E
RUBENIO/*desumptum*/OPUS/ANT. WATEAU

Fig 39–1 Anthony van Dyck *Portrait of Geronima Spinola Doria*, (detail).
Staatliche Museen Preussischer Kulturbesitz, Gemäldegalerie, Berlin

Fig 39-2 After Sir Peter Paul Rubens *Head of a Young Woman*. Musée du
Louvre, Cabinet des Dessins, Paris

Provenance: P.J. Mariette (L. 2097); E. Czeczowiczka; F.
    Koenigs; D.G. van Beuningen
Bibliography: Parker 1931, 26, no. 18; Gradmann 1949, pl. 7;
    Boucher and Jaccottet 1952, no. 17; Parker and Mathey
    1957, I, no. 290; Haverkamp-Begemann 1957, no. 56
Exhibitions: Rotterdam 1934/35, no. 93; Amsterdam 1935,
    no. 43; Paris 1935 (II), no. 175; Rotterdam 1938, no. 381;
    Cologne-Glasgow 1939, no. 53; Paris 1952, no. 71; Rot-
    terdam 1952, no. 127; Paris-Amsterdam 1964, no. 36,
    pl. 46; Paris 1967, no. 278; Washington-Paris-Berlin 1984/
    85, no. 135

Rotterdam, Museum Boymans-van Beuningen. Inv. no. F I 294

Were it not for the seventeenth-century ruff, one would assume this sensitive drawing of an elegant young woman to be a study from life. The sitter's gaze seems to extend beyond the pictorial space to engage our own, yet, Watteau followed Rubens, himself a master of the portrait from life.[1]

The precise source for Watteau's copy has yet to be identified. Van Dyck's *Portrait of Geronima Spinola Doria* (Fig. 39–1), the closest among paintings by Rubens and his circle and frequently mentioned as the source, although similiar in spirit, seems too far removed in aspects like the tilt of the head and the ruff. A drawing formerly in the Péreire collection and now in the Louvre also has been proposed and has been thought to be the one about which Carl Gustaf Tessin wrote: 'I bought this fine head in 1715 in Paris, from the inventory of a collector named Lober. Watteau was charmed by it and he borrowed it from me to copy it several times'.[2] The drawing Tessin owned, however, is not necessarily the one in Paris (Fig. 39–2) which probably was drawn by someone other than Rubens after the same model Watteau copied. The model still is lost.[3]

Watteau created a sensitive and vivacious image by applying open and varied touches of chalk (his preferred *trois crayons*) to define the sitter's hair, eyes, and brows. Her plume and ruffled collar, boldly delineated with the freest of strokes, are paralleled by the predominantly diagonal lines from lower left to upper right. Together they impart a sense of impending motion. Whatever his source, Watteau endowed his image of the young woman with a lightness all his own.

P.V.

---

1   As noted in the inscription on the old mount.

2   C. van Hasselt, in Paris-Amsterdam 1964, no. 36, mentioned it as Watteau's model.

3   Nordenfalk (1953, in Washington-Paris-Berlin 1984/85, 22, and in Nordenfalk 1987), recalled Tessin's note concerning a drawing he presented with others as a Christmas present to Princess Louise-Ulrica in 1746. The note, preserved in the Nationalmuseum, Stockholm, was hypothetically applied by him to the lost example of Watteau's drawing in Rotterdam, here exhibited, and subsequently to the drawing in the Péreire Collection when this was mentioned as the lost example by van Hasselt. The Péreire drawing, now in the Musée du Louvre (inv. no. RF 29736) seems neither a work by Rubens nor by van Dyck. Before Péreire owned it, it had been in the Desperet collection (L. 721).

Antoine Watteau

Valenciennes 1684–Nogent-sur-Marne 1721

40 Bust of a Woman
After Rubens

Trois crayons
  287 × 218 mm
Provenance: N. Beets
Bibliography: Parker and Mathey 1957, I, no. 282; Mongan and
  Sachs 1940, I, no. 487; Held 1959, I, 13
Exhibitions: Amsterdam 1935 no. 44; Providence 1975, no. 39

Private Collection

So masterfully could Watteau capture both the spirit and technique of Rubens's portrait drawings, that Glück and Haberditzl, not knowing this drawing, believed its counter-proof to be by Rubens's hand.[1] Only in 1940 was it attributed to Watteau by Beets, Mongan and Sachs.[2] This drawing and its counter-proof in Vienna are among six known versions, among them Fig. 40–1, none by Rubens.[3] All probably copy a now lost work by Rubens that must have had tremendous power and vitality.

Watteau, in his copy, exploited the *trois crayons* technique to its fullest. He varied the quality of line throughout the image, broken and scumbled for the facial features, hard and straight for the hair, and loose and sketchy for her costume. Furthermore, he interweaved the three chalks to create a sense of atmosphere and overall unity of light without sacrificing the palpability of the model.

Watteau never made direct use of his copies after Rubens's figures in his later works. But only through Rubens did Watteau arrive at his own version of the elegant and refined women who populate the rococo landscape of his *fêtes galantes*.
  P.V.

1   Glück-Haberditzl 1928, no. 228.
2   Mongan and Sachs 1940, I, no. 487.
3   Held 1959, I, 13.

40 Bust of a Woman

Fig 40-1 After Sir Peter Paul Rubens *Head of a Young Woman*. Musée du Louvre, Cabinet Edmond de Rothschild, Paris

41 **Italian Landscape with an old Woman spinning in the Foreground**

Antoine Watteau

Valenciennes 1684–Nogent-sur-Marne 1721

41 Italian Landscape with an old Woman spinning in the Foreground
After Campagnola

Red chalk on cream paper
205 × 318 mm
Provenance: A. de Hevesy; M. Komor; W.C. Baker

Fig 41-1 Domenico Campagnola *Landscape with an old Woman holding a Spindel*. The Metropolitan Museum of Art, New York, bequest of Walter C. Baker, 1971

Bibliography: Parker 1935, 8; Parker and Mathey 1957, I, no. 439; Virch 1962, 43, no. 72
Exhibitions: Washington-Paris-Berlin 1984/85, no. 140

New York, The Metropolitan Museum of Art, bequest of Walter C. Baker. Inv. no. 1972.118.237

In this drawing, as in the majority of his copies after other masters, Watteau used red chalk.[1] By translating Campagnola's pen and ink drawing (Fig. 41−1) into this medium as well as by exploiting the texture of the laid paper in some areas, Watteau obtained freer and softer effects enhancing the qualities of silvery light and far-reaching space. Although Watteau was relatively faithful to the composition of the model, he emphasized atmosphere and nature at the expense of narrative detail. The woman spinning is merely indicated, while the two figures on the left in the middle distance have been omitted entirely.

Watteau may have copied Campagnola's drawing while it

was in the collection of his patron and benefactor, Pierre Crozat. Crozat acquired a large number of Italian drawings during a trip to Italy in 1714/15 and the Campagnola drawing copied here may have been among them.[2] Watteau never visited Italy, but he made a number of studies after Titian and Domenico Campagnola.[3] These landscape sketches were crucial to him in suggesting the appropriate settings for his *commedia dell'arte* paintings.

Watteau took up details from the copy here exhibited in the backgrounds of his paintings *The Love Lesson* (1716/17, Nationalmuseum, Stockholm) and *Country Amusements* (1716/18, Private Collection). Landscape backgrounds in his paintings after 1716 often include Venetian towers, distant mountains, crumbling masonry walls, and similar Italianate motifs.

Watteau was the first French artist of the eighteenth century to be recognized as having copied Italian landscape drawings, so initially every French copy of that period was attributed to him. Though the situation is far from resolved, it is now known that others did the same and drawings once given to Watteau are being reattributed to some of his contemporaries such as Nicholaes Vleughels, who copied Italian landscapes in similar media and techniques.[3] Furthermore, a drawing after Campagnola, once attributed to Watteau, has since been shown to be by Boucher, who utilized it for the setting of a painting now lost but recorded by Saint-Aubin.[4] This demonstrates that a younger generation of artists perpetuated Watteau's practice, one strongly encouraged in French Academic circles.

P.V.

1   Parker and Mathey include over one hundred landscapes in their 1957 catalogue of Watteau drawings. A number of these are direct studies of nature, such as a series of sketches of the gardens of the Luxembourg palace. Over two-thirds of the surviving landscape drawings are copies after Italian masters. See Parker and Mathey 1957.
2   Mariette's catalogue of Crozat's collection included 131 drawings by Campagnola. The collection of the Parisian banker Jabach, which Watteau studied as early as 1712, may also have provided an early source for his study of the works of Campagnola.
3   For example the series of Italianate landscapes in red chalk and green wash attributed to Watteau (Parker and Mathey nos. 376, 402–416, 420, 423–425) has been removed from Watteau's oeuvre by Rosenberg who has suggested an attribution to Vleughels (see Washington-Paris-Berlin 1984/85, 55–56).
4   See Jacoby 1979, 262–263.

François Boucher

Paris 1703–1770

42 Studies of a seated Shepherd Boy and an old Woman standing

After Bloemaert

Red and black chalk
237 × 178 mm
Annotated lower left: *F. Boucher*
Provenance: Comte A.G.P. de Bizemont Prunelé (L. 128); Admiral de Condé
Bibliography: Ananoff and Wildenstein 1976, 228, no. 101/5, fig. 398; Slatkin 1976, 248–249, pl. 2 and cover; New York-Detroit-Paris 1986/87, no. 23, fig. 112; Jacoby 1986, 134 and 136, no. II.c.1, fig. 18
Exhibitions: Copenhagen 1935, no. 537; Bordeaux 1958, no. 46; Orléans-Paris 1975/76, 16, no. 14, pl. LV; Lille 1985, no. 7; Pittsburgh, etc. 1986/87, 11, no. 21

Orléans, Musée des Beaux-Arts d'Orléans. Inv. no. 1146

On this sheet Boucher combined in a free arrangement figures that he found in two separate drawings by Bloemaert. Bloemaert's drawing of the shepherd boy is now lost but the existence of Bloemaert's other drawing *Woman with a Kettle*, in the Hermitage (Fig. 42–1) confirms that Boucher faithfully translated the figure studies. His broad strokes and quick dashes in red chalk capture the salient features of the figures Bloemaert rendered in black chalk, pale green wash, and white highlighting. Thus Boucher noticed and emphasised the lightness and vivacity intimated in Bloemaert's figures.

Boucher may have acquired a set of original drawings during or shortly after his tenure between 1728 and 1731 as a student at the French Academy in Rome.[1] In 1735, Boucher published the *Livre d'Etudes d'après les Dessins originaux de Bloemaert*, twelve etchings that are composites of motifs selected from various study sheets by Bloemaert. Plate 2 depicts the standing old woman and plate 8 (Fig. 42–2) the two seated shepherds, all in reverse.[2] Slatkin has suggested that this red chalk drawing is a preparatory study Boucher made in conjunction with the etchings.[3] It is the only one of its kind hitherto identified.

Boucher used Bloemaert's figures as staffage in his paintings. In the painting of 1734, *A View of the Campo Vaccino*, (Fig. 42–3), he placed the figure of the seated shepherd seen in profile in an Italianate setting based on his own study from nature.[4] In synthesizing these Dutch and Italian elements, Boucher added a rustic note to the landscape with classical ruins. Boucher never forgot the Bloemaert studies. Both his figures and his landscapes exhibit Bloemaert's lasting effect.

P.V.

1   See Slatkin 1976, 247. Pierre Subleyras, a fellow *pensionnaire* in Rome who never returned to France, also copied from the set, including the drawing of the seated shepherd.
2   For a discussion of the Bloemaert drawings in the Hermitage acquired from the Argutinsky-Dolgoruky collection and their relationship to Boucher's suite of etchings, see Kamenskaya 1937. In Boucher's copy of the Hermitage drawing he omitted the seated woman at the right. However, he did include this figure in his set of etchings after Bloemaert.

42 Studies of a seated Shepherd Boy and an old Woman standing

Fig 42-1 Abraham Bloemaert *Woman with a Kettle*. The Hermitage, Leningrad

Fig 42-2 François Boucher *Two seated Shepherd Boys*. Plate 8 from the *Livre d'Etudes*

3   See Slatkin 1976, 247.
4   Voss 1953, 82. New York 1986, 247. Also, the figure of the seated shepherd appears in Bloemaert's two *Tobias and ·the Angel* paintings (Staatliche Museen, Berlin and Kunsthalle, Hamburg), in *The Goatherd* (Earl Spencer Collection) and in *The Preaching of Saint John* (Bayerische Staatsgemäldesammlungen, Schleissheim Collection).

Fig 42-3 François Boucher *A View of the Campo Vaccino*. The Metropolitan
Museum of Art, The Jack and Belle Linsky Collection, New York

Jean-Honoré Fragonard

Grasse 1732–Paris 1806

43 The Funeral of Decius Mus
After Rubens

Brush and brown wash over black chalk on cream laid paper
240 × 376 mm
Provenance: H. Walferdin; Sale, Paris, 12–16 April 1880, no. 240; E. Borthon; Sale, 1890, no. 39; O. Wertheimer; B. Sonnenberg
Bibliography: Portalis 1889, 302; Tornézy 1895, 400; Ananoff 1961–70, II, no. 1098, and IV, 336; Massengale 1979, 271; Sutton 1980, n.p.; *Cleveland* 1981, 190, no. 193
Exhibitions: Providence 1975, no. 54; Washington 1978 (I), no. 34

Cleveland, The Cleveland Museum of Art, Purchase John L. Severance Fund. Inv. no. CMA 80.17

En route from Venice to Paris in 1774 at the end of a year's journey through Italy in the company of the wealthy connoisseur and patron of Boucher, Bergeret de Grandcourt, Fragonard, stopped in a number of cities to see and to sketch from works in the great collections.[1] In Vienna, the main attractions were paintings by Rubens and van Dyck housed in the Liechtenstein Palace, among them, the six large cartoons by Rubens and his studio on the life of the Roman general Decius Mus (1618).[2]

Fragonard was already familiar with Rubens's work before visiting Vienna, having first encountered it while apprenticed (*c.* 1748–52) to Boucher, himself a student of Rubens's colour and female forms.[3] In Italy in 1761, Fragonard had drawn from Rubens's *The Horrors of War* (Pitti Palace) and in 1767 he requested permission to copy the Medici cycle in the Luxembourg Palace. Furthermore, Fragonard may already have known the *Decius Mus* series. His drawing in chalk and wash after *Decius Mus Dismissing the Lictors* is signed and dated 1769.[4] Its static composition differs markedly, however, from the crowded and agitated cartoon he copied here.

In this drawing, Fragonard copied the funeral procession for the fallen Roman General in its entirety.[5] He captured not only the lush decor of the setting and the pronounced musculature of the figures but also accentuated the powerful circular rhythm formed by the human chain in Rubens's composition (Fig. 43–1). While accepting the restrictions of monochromatic wash, he never-theless exploited its potential and achieved great tonal range by modulating the application and the intensity of his colour. He suggested the background funeral pyre in delicate greys and recorded the writhing foreground bodies with crisp contours and bold chiaroscuro.

Fragonard's study after the *Decius Mus* represents the later phase in his career as a copyist, one which illustrates the French artist's compatibility with Rubens's own style.[6] He copied a huge overscale history scene onto a single sheet, yet still managed to make an interpretive statement. Far from his exacting chalk copies of the 1760s, this brilliant wash drawing reflects Fragonard's own mastery of the drawing technique in the face of an extremely complex subject. The long, yet well-controlled brushstrokes anticipate the flowering of Fragonard's late draw-ing style as illustrated by a series of drawings for Ariosto's *Orlando Furioso*, usually dated to the 1780s.[7]

L.K.

1   The diaries of Pierre Jacques Onésyme Bergeret de Grandcourt (Tornézy 1895) are the primary source for the itinerary of the trip. Fragonard first travelled to Italy in 1759–61 with the Abbé de Saint Non whose diaries are republished with illustrations of Fragonard's drawings and an introduction in Rosenberg and Bréjon de Lavergnée 1986.
2   Tornézy 1895, 400. On the cycle, see New York 1985, 338–341.
3   The Goncourt brothers (1882, 336) linked Boucher and Fragonard with respect to Rubens. See also Providence 1975, 147–152.
4   For the copy of *The Horrors of War*, see Ananoff 1961–70, II, no. 1099. Fragonard's request is recorded in a letter from Cochin to Marigny, keeper of the royal collections in Paris. Massengale 1979, 271 discusses the dated drawing (Ananoff 1961–70, II, no. 1019, not described as after Rubens) as after Rubens and suggests that Fragonard possibly sketched copies of the *Decius Mus* series in Brussels before 1773.
5   Most of Fragonard's earlier chalk copies after the old masters are only partial copies of the original compositions. In this, and in the copy after van Dyck (Cat. no. 44), Fragonard has captured the entire image on his sheet.
6   For a chronology of Fragonard's drawing techniques, see Mongan 1945, and Williams in Washington 1978 (I), no. 34, and 22–23. Fragonard's interest in Rubens may have developed in tandem with use of the wash technique, for it was in the late 1760s and early 1770s that he began making complete copies after works by Rubens.
7   Mongan 1945, and Williams in Washington 1978 (I), no. 34.

43 **The Funeral of Decius Mus**

Fig 43-1 Sir Peter Paul Rubens *The Obsequies of Decius Mus*. Collections of
the Prince of Liechtenstein, Vaduz Castle, Vaduz

44 Achilles among the Daughters of Lycomedes

Jean-Honoré Fragonard

Grasse 1732–Paris 1806

44 Achilles among the Daughters of Lycomedes
After van Dyck

Pen and brown wash
400 × 470 mm
Provenance: C. Naudet; Sale, 5 January 1869; Mme. de Bayser;
   H.S. Schaeffer
Bibliography: Ananoff 1961–70, II, no. 1069, fig. 285
Exhibition: Los Angeles 1961, no. 49

New York, Mrs Rush Kress

Achilles among the Daughters of Lycomedes depicts the discovery of
Achilles, who disguised as a woman among the daughters of the
King of Syros, revealed his identity by selecting the sword from
a coffer full of jewellery presented to the daughters. Fragonard
copied this grand mythological subject as van Dyck interpreted
it in a painting for Prince Frederick Henry of Orange in The
Hague, on one of his two trips to Holland (1628/29 and 1632).[1]
Mentioned in an inventory of August 1632 as a bedroom
chimneypiece, it is now considered by van Gelder to be lost.[2]
Which of the several replicas Fragonard copied is not clear; it
may have been the one now in the collection of Miss Clara Colwell, London (Fig. 44–1) since it corresponds most closely to the
drawing with respect to the setting and number of figures.[3]
Where he could have seen it, however, is not known.

As in Cat. no. 43, Fragonard transcribed the scene in its
entirety, vastly reducing its scale to accommodate the smaller
size of the sheet. Fragonard had made the same transition
between media in copies after his own oil sketches for his early
historical paintings.[4] In the present drawing, Fragonard carefully translated the overall appearance of van Dyck's painting,
but freely interpreted the drapery folds, redistributing light and
dark accents. More significant, however, is his transformation
of the size of the figures. In proportion to the setting, he enlarged
them all, even the dog at the right, thereby bringing them closer
to the viewer.

Fragonard painted few multi-figured historical scenes but
drew numerous literary and genre subjects full of drama and
action, independent of his painted oeuvre. This exploration of
the manner in which figures convey narrative therefore relates
more to Fragonard's work as a draughtsman than as a painter.
Perhaps to gain experience for these drawings, he made this and
other copies, translating the intricate interaction of figures into
their equivalent in wash. Stylistically, this drawing must date
to the 1770s.[5]
   L.K.

Fig 44-1 After Anthony van Dyck *Achilles among the Daughters of Lycomedes*.
Collection Clara Colwell, London

1   Glück 1931, no. 264; Larsen 1980, no. 610, 610A; van Gelder 1959,
56–57.
2   This inventory is reprinted in van Gelder 1959, 53–55.
3   *Ibid*, 56. Van Gelder considers the London version to be the best existing
replica of the lost work. Unfortunately, the earlier provenance of this painting is unknown. Other versions include paintings in Toulouse, Stockholm,
and Schloss Schönbrunn (Pommersfelden). Larsen 1980, 610 believes that

the Pommersfelden version, which was already installed there by 1719, is
the original.
4   The precise reason for his making these copies is unclear, but it is thought
he made them as records. Washington 1978 (I), nos. 18 and 19.
5   The drawing is similar to others dating from this decade, *Head of an
Oriental* (Besançon 1956, no. 74, pl. XVI) or *Grandfather's Reprimand*
(Washington 1978 (I), no. 46).

45 **Figure before the Arch of Drusus**

Hubert Robert

Paris 1733–1808

45 Figure before the arch of Drusus

From François Boucher

Red chalk on white paper, laid down
285 × 370 mm
Inscribed lower left margin in pen: *Robert le merc 11 janvier 1775*;
annotated on the mount: *Arc de Drusus à Rome*
Provenance: J.-V. Veyrenc
Bibliography: Nolhac and Loukomski 1930, pl. 10; Beau 1968,
no. 14
Exhibitions: Washington 1978 (II), no. 40; Bordeaux 1961,
no. 233; Paris 1969, no. 14

Valence, Le Musée de Valence. Inv. no. D. 117

This scene of a peasant girl driving her donkey under a partly
buried Roman ruin is an assemblage of motifs from two disparate
sources. The ruin is a romanticized, imaginery view of the fully-
excavated Arch of Drusus which Hubert Robert would have
derived from memory, a drawing from his Italian years or an
engraving.[1] Robert took the figures, with some modification,
from a painting by Boucher of 1770 *Le Retour du marché* (Fig. 45–
1), appropriately described by Ananoff as 'in the manner of
Berchem'.[2] Later in life, Robert is thought to have resorted to
the work of the *premier peintre* as a model on which to base his
figures previously criticized by Diderot for their weakness.[3]

The high degree of finish indicates that this drawing of 1775
is an independent work of art. The identical figural group, however, reappears in two undated paintings by Robert, *La Cascade*
(collection Jean Cailleux, Paris) and *Le Colisée et l'arc de Constantin*
(Musée d'Avignon).[4] A parallel case of Robert's borrowing
directly from Boucher in both a drawing and a painting was
noted by Cailleux in 1959.[5]

As in Cat. no. 43, we know that Boucher, too, incorporated
figures borrowed from other artists, namely Bloemaert, as staffage in his paintings.[6] Thus by weaving figures ultimately Dutch
in origin into settings based on the Roman campagna, Robert
perpetuated the practice of his French predecessor while
responding to Diderot's valuation of pictorial unity over
imitation.[7]

C.L.

Fig 45-1 François Boucher *Le Retour du marché*. Location unknown

1   The exact source for the arch has not been established, see Washington
1978 (II), no. 40.
2   Ananoff 1976, II, no. 690.
3   Beau 1968, no. 14.
4   Reproduced in Beau 1968, figs. 14e and f.
5   Cailleux 1959, 100–101. Both Beau and Cailleux have singled out drawings containing figures executed by Robert in the manner of Boucher, see
Beau 1968, nos. 62 and 66, and Paris 1978, no. 48. Ananoff has pointed to
a series of painted collaborations, Boucher animating Robert's landscapes
with picturesque groups of figures, see Ananoff 1976, II, 327, fig. 1797, for
example.
6   Voss 1953, 82 and Slatkin 1976, 247–260.
7   Lochhead 1982, 27–28.

46 The Mocking of Christ

Louis-Jacques Durameau

Paris 1733–Versailles 1796

46 The Mocking of Christ
After David de Haen

Red chalk heightened with white on beige paper
199 × 405 mm
Provenance: P.J. Mariette (L. 2097): H.M. Calmann
Bibliography: Sandoz 1980, no. 13d

Fig 46-1 David de Haen *Mocking of Christ*. San Pietro in Montorio, Rome

Exhibitions: Paris 1967, no. 228; Amsterdam 1974, no. 33; Lille 1985, no. 47

Amsterdam, Rijksmuseum, Rijksprentenkabinet. Inv. no. 1952: 70

Of the four extant works of *c.* 1617 by Dirck van Baburen and David de Haen decorating the Pietà Chapel of San Pietro in Montorio, Durameau copied the least baroque (Fig. 46–1).[1] In drawing de Haen's *Mocking of Christ*, he deemphasized the strong raking light which imparts a sense of high drama to the work of this Dutch Caravaggist and focussed instead on the manner in which the narrative is expressed through gesture and facial expression. Durameau paid close attention to detail in rendering the polarized figures, disposed in a frieze-like manner. Even though he repeated the semi-circular frame dictated by the architectural setting, Durameau conveys the impression of having copied only a fragment from a larger painting.

Durameau made this copy during his stay at the French Academy in Rome from 1761 to 1764 expressly for Mariette. Commissioned by the great *amateur* to make copies after paintings by various old masters not yet known through engravings, it numbers among others after Mola, Gaulli, and Solimena.[2] All are in red chalk, fully pictorial, and similarly faithful to their

models. They are an independent entity within the artists oeuvre.

While director of the French Academy in Rome from 1751 to 1777, Natoire also made drawings for Mariette after artists such as Lodovico Caracci, Guercino, Castiglione, and Gaulli.[3] These copies served as *aides-mémoire* for the author of the *Abecedario* while copies after more contemporary artists, Luti or Trevisani, drawn mainly by Durameau, helped Mariette keep abreast of developments in Roman art.[4]

C.L.

1   Reproduced in Slatkes 1965, figs. 1, 5, 6, and 7.
2   See Sandoz 1980, no. 13 where some of the copies are reproduced.
3   See Troyes-Nîmes-Rome 1977, 29 and no. 78.
4   For a discussion of Mariette as a collector, see Bacou 1967.

47 The Water-Bearer

Benjamin West

Philadelphia 1738–London 1820

47 The Water-Bearer
After Raphael's fresco

Black chalk on pinkish-brown prepared paper
580 × 420 mm
Provenance: R.L. West; M. West; H. Margary
Exhibitions: New York 1975, no. 202, pl. 106; Washington
   1983, 17, fig. 2, no. 3

New York, The Pierpont Morgan Library. Inv. no. 1970.11:248

In a letter of *c.* 1788, West advised a pupil of his on a course
of study in Italy that replicated his own experience there twenty
years earlier. He recommended above all studying and copying
the antique, Michelangelo, and Raphael.[1] The drawing of *The
Water-Bearer* documents West's own careful study of Raphael
(Fig. 47–1), when in Rome between 1760 and 1763. He meticulously rendered the model paying close attention to the fall
of light and shade and to the details of fluttering drapery without
sacrificing the solidity of the figure. When Manet copied the
same figure a century later, he too emphasized its plasticity and
monumentality but did so in an abbreviating manner with broad
and rapid strokes in red chalk (Fig. 47–2).[2]
     For his copy, West used black chalk on pinkish-brown pre-
pared paper in imitation of the Renaissance practice. Three
small sketchbooks, now in the Royal Academy in London, and
a group of drawings at Swarthmore College contain representations of architecture, sculpture, and portions of paintings
sketched during this period. The copy after the *Fire in the Borgo*
is related in size, media, and preparation to drawings after
Michelangelo's frescoes in the Sistine Chapel, including the
Adam from the *Creation of Eve* and three figures from the *Deluge*.[3]
In contrast to these drawings, West applied a linear technique
emphasizing contours for copies after the antique.
     West incorporated many of his studies into his paintings.
Agrippina and her entourage in the work of 1768, *Agrippina Land-
ing at Brundesium with the Ashes of Germanicus* (Yale University Art
Gallery, New Haven) derive directly from his study of the proces-
sional relief on the Ara Pacis. But the figure of the water-bearer
never was reflected in his later work.
     P.V.

Fig 47-1 Raphael *Fire in the Borgo*, (detail). Stanze dell'Incendio, Vatican,
Rome

1   Forster-Hahn 1967, 367.
2   De Leiris 1969, 48, no. 24, fig. 89.
3   See New York 1975, nos. 199, 200, 201, and 203.

Fig 47-2 Edouard Manet *The Water-Bearer*. Musée du Louvre, Cabinet des Dessins, Paris

Henry Fuseli

Zürich 1741–London 1825

48 Woman contemplating the Laocoon
After the antique

Pencil, pen and brown ink, brush and brown wash
320 × 404 mm
Verso: Another sketch of the Laocoon
Bibliography: Federmann 1927, pl. 42; Irwin 1966, 48; Tomoroy 1972, 180–181; Schiff 1973, 227, 547, no. 1072; Keay 1974
Exhibitions: Zürich 1926, no. 225; Zürich 1941, no. 332; London 1975, no. 188.; Milan 1977, no. 27; Tokyo 1983, no. 89

Zürich, Kunsthaus. Inv. no. 1913/7

Fuseli almost certainly knew and copied the *Laocoon* during his stay in Rome in the 1770s. Nevertheless, references to the sculpture only appear in his work after 1802 when he saw the monument again in Paris. This drawing, made on a sheet with a watermark dated 1801, may be the earliest extant record of Fuseli's renewed interest in the sculpture.[1]

The drawing is not a precise copy of the antique sculpture (Fig. 48–1). Fuseli eliminated the sons altogether and reduced the snakes to an abbreviated reference. Moreover, he accentuated the physical tension of the figure of Laocoon through subtle changes in pose and musculature. For instance, Fuseli shortened the length of Laocoon's torso, raised the height of his right arm and placed his head further back on his shoulders. These changes combine to make the arc of Laocoon's body, and the strain of the musculature, appear even more severe than they do in the original. In his *Fifth Lecture on Painting*, delivered in 1802 shortly before his trip to Paris, Fuseli wrote that the *Laocoon* is the supreme ancient example of the 'convulsed', one of the five ideal types of external expression in art.[2] The changes in the drawing appear to emphasize this interpretation of the monument.

The most significant change, however, is the addition of the courtesan at the left. Tomoroy believed this was intended as a satire of the artist Maria Cosway.[3] There is little to substantiate this idea. Rather, the added figure may reflect the chronic and deeply personal interests of Fuseli himself. People watching others suffer are common in Fuseli's work, beginning with the Dante illustrations of the 1770s. Moreover, the sexual implications of the drawing are consistent with those of Fuseli's contemporary works which often show women teasing men in bondage.[4]

Throughout the eighteenth and nineteenth centuries, the *Laocoon* was at the centre of debate on the limits of the visual and literary arts. Winckelmann, Lessing, Goethe and Reynolds discussed the sculpture in this regard.[5] Only William Blake, however, interpreted the *Laocoon* in a fashion as personal and eccentric as Fuseli's. The *Laocoon* served Blake in an engraving c. 1818 (Fig. 48–2) as an allegory of the enslavement of imagination and art by science, bad government, and false religion.[6]

A.B.

1   Watermark: 'S & D 1801'; Schiff 1973, no. 1072.
2   Knowles 1831, 258.
3   Tomoroy 1972, 180.
4   See G. Schiff, 'Fuseli, Lucifer and the Medusa', in London 1975, 9–20.
5   For the critical history of the *Laocoon*, with further citations, see Haskell and Penny 1981, 243–247.

6   For Blake's print, see Bindman 1978, cat. no. 623. Further information on the theoretical intentions behind the print, see Erdmann 1969 and Eaves 1982.

48 Woman contemplating the Laocoon

Fig 48-1 *Laocoon*. Vatican Museum, Rome

Fig 48-2 William Blake *Laocoon*. Collection of Geoffrey Keynes

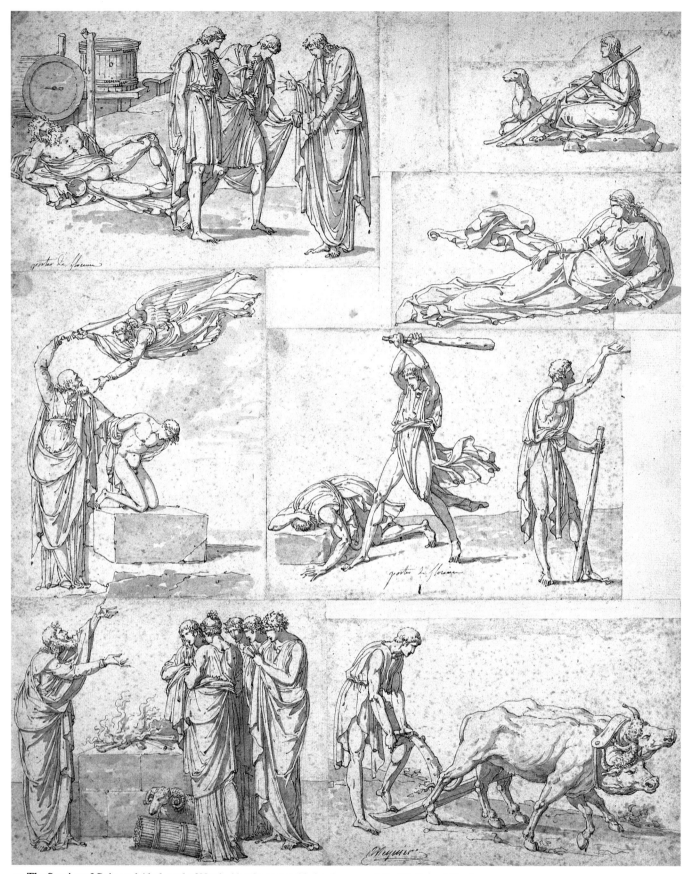

49 The Stories of Cain and Abel, and of Noah, Abraham sacrificing Isaac, and the Mother of Noah

Charles Meynier

Paris 1768–1832

49 The Stories of Cain and Abel, and of Noah, Abraham sacrificing Isaac, and the Mother of Noah
From Ghiberti's bronze doors for the Florence Baptistry

Brown ink and brown wash; seven sketches pasted on one sheet
547 × 440 mm

Fig 49-1 Lorenzo Ghiberti *The Story of Cain and Abel*, a panel from the bronze doors of the Florence Baptistry

Signed at lower centre: *Meynier*; inscribed twice, at upper left
    and in the centre: *portes de florence*
Provenance: H. and S. Baderou
Bibliography: Vilain 1980, 116 and n. 43
Exhibition: Washington 1981/82, no. 76

Rouen, Musée des Beaux-Arts. Inv. no. 975.4.1412

In Ghiberti's *Gates of Paradise* for the Florence Baptistry (Fig. 49–1) Meynier found a model of narrative representation which he transformed in accordance with Davidian rules of formulating figures, draperies, and movement. The subtle attenuation of the figures, the idiosyncratic convention for the rendering of profiles, and the nervous stroke of the pen are in accordance with these precepts, and at the same time betray the hand of Meynier.[1] The copies record none of Ghiberti's innovations in depth of modelling, proportion and setting, which clarify the continuous narrative and spatial recession in each panel.[2] This group of seven studies after Ghiberti represents an ideal neo-classical reformulation of bas-relief sculpture into two-dimensional, shaded, linear forms.

Meynier's studies date from his student years at the French Academy in Rome: from 1789 when he tied with Girodet for the Prix de Rome to 1793 when the Academy was disbanded.[3] Never fully incorporated into subsequent works, the studies provided a vocabulary of gestures which Meynier reused frequently.[4]

Comparison with studies after Ghiberti's Bapistry doors by J.-G. Drouais (Fig. 49–2), the short-lived and highly talented contemporary of David, affirms the standardization in training of pupils at the French Academy. Just like his compatriot, Drouais imposed his neo-classical vision on the relief sculpture, isolating figures or groups for study of drapery and gesture with little concern for perspective or plasticity.[5] Seurat also made studies from the same reliefs (Fig. 49–3) that, in spite of the fundamental innovations he contributed almost a century later, are remarkably similar to those by Meynier and other classicists.[6]

C.L.

Fig 49-2 Jean-Germain Drouais after Ghiberti *Study of Two Figures*, Musée des Beaux-Arts de Rennes

1   Compare with his drawings reproduced in Paris 1974/75, 94–96.
2   See Krautheimer 1971, 3–9.
3   For a reproduction of the Prix de Rome sketch, *Joseph Recognized by his Brothers*, see Paris 1973, no. 27. Another sheet with a sketch after the Baptistry doors is in the Metropolitan Museum of Art, New York, inv. no. 60.66.12.
4   Compare the gesture of Noah sacrificing with that of Marshal Ney in Meynier's painting of 1808, *Marshal Ney and the Soldiers of the 76th Regiment, at Versailles*, reproduced in Paris-Detroit-New York 1975, no. 129, pl. 198.
5   For discussion and reproduction, see Rennes 1985, 69, figs. 6–10, and nos. 297–306.
6   See Herbert 1962, figs. 29 and 30. Delacroix also copied figures from reproductions of the Baptistry doors, Musée du Louvre, RF 9141, reproduced in Sérullaz 1984, II, no. 1738, folio 10v and 11r.

Fig 49-3 Georges Seurat after Ghiberti *Male Figure*. Location unknown

50 The Bacchus Richelieu

Jean-August-Dominique Ingres

Montauban 1780–Paris 1867

50 The Bacchus Richelieu
After the antique

Charcoal with stumping, slightly accented with black chalk on cream wove paper
728 × 520 mm
Annotated by Mme. Ingres in pen and brown ink, upper right quadrant: *Ve Ingres*. Inscribed and dated in black chalk, upper right corner: *J D Ingres 1793*
Provenance: Mme Ingres; L. Bonnal; Mme A. Bonnal-Monfleur; P. Bianchini; Sale, Christie's, London, 23 June 1970, no. 148, illus., [called Bust of a Bacchante]
Bibliography: Hattis 1973, 58–60 [*c.* 1791–93]

New York, The Forbes Magazine Collection. Inv. no. P70020-D

In French Academies of the eighteenth and nineteenth centuries, the second phase of drawing instruction was the *dessin en bosse*, or drawing after the plaster cast.[1] The aims of this instruction were to teach the student three-dimensional modelling and to make him sensitive to the effects of light and shade. A plaster cast of an antique or modern sculpture would be placed under strong light so that its surface would be marked by sharp contrasts of light and dark. The student would then draw the cast using a range of chalks, charcoal, and an *estompe*, a cylindrical rubbing device wrapped in soft paper. The drawings were to be vigorous in effect, yet carefully modelled. Especial emphasis was placed on tonal balance achieved by the use of *demi-teintes*, or half-tones.

Both in conception and technique Ingres' drawing is a distinguished example of the *dessin en bosse*.[2] He chose to depict the sculpture from an angle so that more light falls on the distant side of the face while the prominent side is in greater shadow. Such a relation of bust to light-source is rare among *dessins en bosse* because of the added difficulties in modelling and chiaroscuro it poses: by tonal range alone the artist must differentiate shaded surfaces and receding lighted areas. Ingres' ambitiousness and sophistication are also clear in his great care to record how the skin of the sculpture absorbs or reflects the light. Moreover, although Ingres' model was almost certainly made of plaster, in his drawing he has deliberately given it the sheen and lustre of marble.

Another copy by Ingres of the bust exists.[3] Although identical in viewpoint, it is slightly smaller in size, and simpler in execution than the drawing in the Forbes Magazine Collection. In the other copy, Ingres attempted to record only the principal forms and the dominant lights and shadows. The range of *demi-teintes* is, consequently, less elaborate. Presumably, that copy served as a preliminary step towards the more finished drawing exhibited here.

The cast Ingres copied was of the so-called *Bacchus Richelieu* (Fig. 50–1). This sculpture entered the public domain in 1794 and plaster casts of the monument are first documented in the same year.[4] It is likely Ingres copied the bust in 1794 or slightly later despite the inscription of 1793 in the drawing's upper right corner. As Hattis has shown,[5] other drawings Ingres dated in the same hand to 1793 are demonstrably later in origin.

Ingres' attitude towards copying sculpture differed markedly from that of artists of earlier centuries. As noted above, Ingres took the greatest care to render the marmoreal appearance of the original, even when, faced with a plaster cast, this required an act of fiction. This could not differ more from the aims of the likes of Rubens, for whom 'any hint of stoniness'[6] destroyed the beauty of a copy of sculpture.

A.B.

Fig 50-1 *Bacchus Richelieu*, (detail). Musée du Louvre, Paris

1   Boime 1971, 22–36 outlines French Academic drawing instruction.
2   See Hattis 1973 for a discussion of the relation of Ingres' drawing style to academic instruction.
3   Hattis 1973, 54–57.
4   Hattis 1973, 57. From 1794 to 1797/98, the sculpture was situated in the Musée des Monuments Français before being transferred to the Musée du Louvre.
5   Hattis 1973, 11.
6   See Muller 1982, for the most extensive analysis of Rubens's *De imitatione statuarum*.

Jean-August-Dominique Ingres

Montauban 1780–Paris 1867

51 Portrait of Henry VIII
After Hans Holbein the Younger

Pencil
240 × 175 mm
Signed: *Holbein pinxit Ingres Del Roma*; inscribed at bottom: *peint*

Fig 51-1 Hans Holbein *Portrait of King Henry VIII*, (replica). Windsor Castle, Windsor

par Holbein/Henry VIII d'Angleterre; inscribed colour notes in drawing itself: *noir, vert, gris*, etc.

Provenance: E. Haro (L. 1241); Sale, Hôtel Drouot, Paris, 6 May 1867, no. 86; N. Beets; Sale, Sotheby's, London, 10 June 1931, no. 72; P. & D. Colnaghi; R. von Hirsch; Sale, Sotheby's, London, 27 June 1978, no. 802

Bibliography: Galichon 1861, 362; Lapauze 1911, 553; Mireur 1911, 10, no. 86; d'Agen 1926, xii; Mathey 1945, 11, repr.; Alazard 1950, pl. XV; Mathey 1955, no. 27; Radius and Camesasca 1968, 120, repr.

Exhibitions: Basel 1943, no. 221; Tübingen-Brussels 1986, no. 77

Zürich, M. Feilchenfeldt

51 Portrait of Henry VIII

The mastery of draughtsmanship and depth of characterization in this magnificent portrait of Henry VIII confirms Ingres' place next to Holbein as a portraitist of the highest stature.[1] With strokes of the pencil so fine and so profuse as to emulate the effect of silverpoint, Ingres translated onto paper Holbein's jewel-like rendering of the King, capturing not only his likeness but also the wealth of detail in his lavishly ornamented costume. The power of the drawing rests partly on an underlying affinity between Ingres style of drawing and Holbein's technique of painting. Both artists understood how to use line to both representational and abstract ends and how to use unmodulated passages to suggest both solid and void simultaneously.

Ingres copied Holbein's portrait while in Rome; he signed the drawing as he did his portraits: . . . *Ingres Del Roma*. The drawing may date from the first of his two stays, between 1806 and 1820. Particularly after 1815, with the fall of Napoleon and the departure of his French patrons from Rome, Ingres made numerous portrait drawings of fashionable foreigners who travelled there. Though he made little of these portraits later in life, preferring historical subjects, it is thought that he valued them greatly.[2] This copy shares with these pencil portraits a marked contrast between the meticulous rendering of facial features and the more summary treatment of dress.

The exact source for Ingres' drawing has not been established. Holbein's portrait of Henry VIII, standing frontally and looking directly outwards, exists only in copies, the vast number of which have not been catalogued. Among the contemporary copies of three-quarter length are two types, one at Windsor (Fig. 51–1) which followed the wall painting at Whitehall, and another represented by the version now in the Galleria Nazionale in Rome, which copied a variant perhaps intended as a pendant to the portrait of Queen Jane Seymour in Vienna.[3] Differences with respect to the King's costume indicate that Ingres copied not the version in Rome but probably an uncatalogued posthumous copy after the painting in Whitehall.

Already before his departure for Rome, Ingres manifested an interest in the art of the past, particularly that which is linear in style. This he shared with other students in David's studio, the more extreme faction known as the Primitifs. At the Salon of 1806, his *Napoleon Enthroned* (Musée de l'Armée) was remarked upon for its 'Gothic' qualities and compared by contemporary critics to Jan van Eyck's *God the Father*, then on exhibition in the Musée Napoléon.[4] Ingres' royal portrait of Napoleon, with its symmetrical, hieratic composition and tight linear technique describing features and textures in minute detail, is also comparable to Holbein's style. Ingres would return to this type of composition and technique again in later paintings, *Jupiter and Thetis* (1811, Musée Granet, Aix-en-Provence) and the *Apotheosis of Homer* (1827, Musée du Louvre).[5]

Throughout his life Ingres admired Holbein. Even in his eighties, he copied a portrait attributed to Holbein and inscribed it: 'Les portraits de Holbein sont au-dessus de tout; il n'y a que ceux de Raphael qui les surpassent'. Such praise from the great admirer of Raphael is matched only by the tribute paid in this drawing which Ingres retained among his possessions until shortly before his death.[6]

C.L.

1   Ingres' reputation as a portraitist was compared to Holbein's by Naef 1967/68.
2   For a catalogue of the portrait drawings, see Naef 1977–80 and the review by Ternois 1980.
3   Strong 1969, I, 158–159, Type V, and no. 4027, and Ganz 1961, no. 96, pl. 137.
4   Rosenblum 1967 (I), 17–37 and colour plate 7.
5   Rosenblum 1967 (I), colour plates 15 and 35.
6   Lapauze 1911, 527–528 and 553.

Francisco de Goya y Lucientes

Fuendetodos 1746–Bordeaux 1828

52 Three Pairs of Hooded Figures
After Flaxman's illustrations to Dante

India ink on buff coloured laid paper; laid down
176 × 262 mm
Provenance: J. Goya; M. Goya; V. Carderera (L. 431)
Bibliography: De Barcia 1906, no. 1275; Rosenblum 1967 (II),
177–178, fig. 206; Gassier and Wilson 1971, no. 761; Symmons 1971, 511, fig. 17; Gassier 1975, 514, fig. 341; Symmons 1984, 234–236, 247, 249–250, fig. 81
Exhibitions: Paris 1961/62, no. 149 (with previous exhibitions);
London 1979, no. 199

Madrid, Biblioteca Nacional. Inv. B. 1275

In five drawings after Flaxman's illustrations to Dante's *Divine Comedy*, Goya with brush and India ink wash transformed these neo-classical line engravings into mysterious, darkly shadowed scenes.[1] In the present drawing, Goya combined figures from two different plates: the three pairs of standing figures derive from plate 25, *Caiaphas and the Hypocrites* (Fig. 52–1), illustrating Canto 23 of the *Inferno*; the crouching figure who replaces the crucified Caiaphas is Dante from plate 28, *The Flaming Gulph*, for Canto 26. Goya faithfully followed the contours of Flaxman's figures but eliminated some details and introduced shaded areas which – as in the edge of the hooded cloaks that are turned as if to acknowledge our presence, for example – intensify the haunting quality suggested by Flaxman.

Flaxman's drawings, engraved by Thomas Piroli, were first issued in Rome in 1793 but were not officially published until 1802.[2] The copies date from 1795,[3] so Goya must have been familiar with a rare first edition. In 1796/97, Goya began working on the *Caprichos*, published in 1799. The menacing anonymity of hooded cloaks and rhythmic repetition of figures in this series is anticipated by these washed transformations of Flaxman's drawings. This dialogue undoubtedly contributed to the genesis of Goya's satyrical, sometimes hallucinatory, comments on society.[4]

J.C.

---

1   Three of these, including the present, are in the Biblioteca Nacional, Madrid, a fourth is in a French private collection, and the fifth is in the Prado; see Gassier and Wilson 1971, nos. 340–342, 344–345, respectively. Gassier and Wilson also discuss another drawing (1971, no. 343) in the Biblioteca Nacional in which Goya used Flaxman as a starting point for the drawing. Symmons does not include it among Goya's copies after Flaxman.
2   Symmons 1971, 277; editions were published in 1802 in Rome and Paris.
3   One of these drawings (Gassier and Wilson 1971, no. 345) was dated by Goya, January 1795; this was first published by de Salas 1971, 34–36. Until this drawing came to light, this group had been dated to 1802–05, presumably copied after the more widely available second edition of 1802. This drawing was also inscribed by Carderera as being a copy after Flaxman.
4   Gassier 1975, 511–512; see also Symmons 1984, 248–250.

52 **Three Pairs of Hooded Figures**

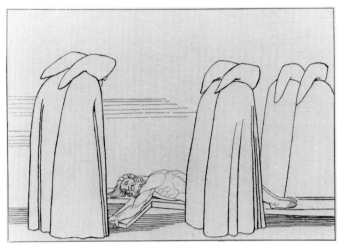

Fig 52-1 Thomas Piroli after John Flaxman *Caiaphas and the Hypocrites.*
Plate 25 from Canto 23 of Dante's *Inferno* 1807 ed

53 **Landscape with Hermit**

Thomas Girtin

London 1775–1802

53 Landscape with Hermit

After an etching by Herman van Swanevelt

Watercolour

333 × 476 mm

Signed and dated lower right: *Girtin – 1801 – Paris*

Provenance: Col. F.C. Maisey

Bibliography: Davies 1928, 221–222, pl. IIA; Mayne 1949, 60 and 98; Girtin and Loshak 1954, 80–81 no. 456, fig. 85; Maison 1966, 23, pl. XII; Morris 1986, 18

Exhibitions: Manchester-London 1975, no. 95 (with further references)

London, The Board of the Trustees of the Victoria and Albert Museum. Inv. no. WD.145

Girtin's landscape is so characteristic of early nineteenth-century British watercolour that at first glance its source in an etching *Rest on the Flight into Egypt* (Fig. 53–1) by Herman van Swanevelt is not apparent. Girtin exploits the nature of watercolour and subordinates the detail of the engraving to an atmospheric view made dramatic by the contrasts in both light and scale. Thereby he lends a new sense of the picturesque to the Italianate landscape of his predecessor.

Two other interpretations by Girtin of Swanevelt's landscape etchings have been identified.[1] All date from a trip to Paris in 1801 and represent the culmination of Girtin's practice of copying prints in watercolour. His transformations of Piranesi and Marco Ricci from the late 1790s parallel in architecture his studies of landscape through Swanevelt. These copies mark a break with the topographical studies of his early years, best exemplified by his outline copies in pen after Canaletto.[2]

Few other interpretative copies after Swanevelt by British watercolourists are known. But the practice of copying landscapes was not uncommon. Turner's choice of Alpine views of 1802, if not dictated, was strongly influenced by his earlier copies (made in collaboration with Girtin) for Dr. Munro after J.R. Cozens's drawings.[3] Constable made a straight copy after a rare print by Swanevelt to supplement his collection of 163 prints by the Dutch Italianate.[4]

C.L.

Fig 53-1 Herman van Swanevelt *Rest on the Flight into Egypt*. Rijksprentenkabinet, Amsterdam

---

1   See Davies 1928, 218 and 223, pls. IA and IIIA.

2   For copies after Piranesi, see Girtin and Loshak 1954, nos. 302–305, after Marco Ricci, nos. 306–310, after Canaletto, nos. 4, 114–117, 221, and especially 224.

3   See Butlin 1962, 7–8.

4   Reproduced in Reynolds 1984, no. 29.11, pl. 709.

54 Trees and Deer

John Constable

East Bergholt, Suffolk 1776–London 1837

54 Trees and Deer
After Claude Lorrain

Pen and brown ink with grey and brown wash on off-white laid
  paper
290 × 200 mm
Inscribed on the *verso* in lead pencil, badly rubbed: *copied from*

Fig 54-1 Claude Lorrain *Trees*. Musée du Louvre, Cabinet Edmond de
Rothschild, Paris

a drawing by Claude Lorraine/left to Sir Thos Lawrence/Hampstead
  July/1825; annotated above in pen and brown ink: *Copied*
  by J. Constable ARA – from a drawing by (as/ – it is said) Claude
  Lorraine,/done at Hooke's Cottage/Hempd. July/1825
Provenance: Dr. J. Percy; L.G. Duke; Colnaghi; P. Mellon
Bibliography: Röthlisberger 1969, 426–427, pl. 32; Rhyne 1981,
  135–136, no. 31, pl. 12; Rosenthal 1983, fig. 186; Reynolds
  1984, no. 25.19, pl. 590 (with further references); Cormack
  1986, fig. 153
Exhibition: New Haven 1977, no. 159 (with further references)

New Haven, Yale Center for British Art, Paul Mellon Collection.
  Inv. no. B1977.14.5223

The striking quality of this drawing lies in the degree to which Constable precisely reproduces a work by Claude Lorrain which he encountered in the collection of Sir Thomas Lawrence in 1825. Röthlisberger's suggestion that Constable adhered not only to the subject matter and composition but to the technique as well was confirmed when Claude's drawing came to light (Fig. 54–1).[1] The penwork used in combination with wash, as well as the use of brown inks mimics Claude's drawing from nature of *c.* 1640 (Cabinet Edmond de Rothschild). Constable's use of old paper suggests that he sought to create a facsimile for a collector or perhaps for himself 'to be useful', as he once wrote in reference to another copy after Claude, 'to me as long as I live'.[2] Indeed, Constable developed a reputation as a connoisseur of Claude and was called upon in 1835 to give evidence on a disputed work.[3]

Constable's fidelity to the source demonstrates his admiration for Claude whose technique clearly affected his work from this time on.[4] In his drawings from nature, such as *Harnham Bridge* (1827), Constable would often combine pen and wash and render foliage in a feathery manner reminiscent of Claude's works. Paintings such as *Dedham Vale* (1828, National Gallery of Scotland) have a measured spatial recession and include *repoussoir* elements which illustrate Constable's application of Claude's compositional principles.[5]

In its faithfulness to the style of Claude's drawing, this copy differs from the numerous sketches Constable made as souvenirs of paintings by such artists as Cuyp, Ruisdael and Claude exhibited at the British Institution in the 1810s. Rather, the drawing relates to the painted replicas he made for collectors.[6] The practice of copying works of art at the request of others was a common one with a long tradition in Britain.

Whereas the influence of Claude on eighteenth-century painters on the Continent has not been fully examined,[7] his importance for British artists has never been underestimated. From Richard Wilson's reinterpretations of the Italianate landscape to Turner's copies, Claude's paintings and drawings lie at the heart of the British landscape tradition.[8]

C.L.

1   See Röthlisberger 1969, 426–427 and for the publication of Claude's drawing, Rosenberg 1971, 116, fig. 17.
2   Beckett 1964, II, 295.
3   See Reynolds 1984, I, no. 35.8; and Beckett 1966, IV, 168–170, 1967, V, 186.
4   See Cormack 1986, 153.
5   See Reynolds 1984, I, nos. 27.45 and 28.1, and II, figs. 674 and 677.
6   For the copies of works seen on exhibition, see Reynolds 1984, nos. 18.32–33; 19.18; 19.19; and for the replicas for the collectors, nos. 23.36–37; 31.15.
7   A welcome step in that direction was the exhibition, Munich 1983, and its catalogue.
8   On Claude's influence in England, see Howard 1969, 726–732; and on Turner, in particular, Michael Kitson, in Paris 1981/1982, 579–597.

Théodore Géricault

Rouen 1791–Paris 1824

55 Fall of the Rebel Angels
From Suyderhoef's engraving after Rubens

Pencil

205 × 232 mm

Provenance: E. Devéria

Bibliography: Facsimiles 1825, pl. 15; Clément 1879, 420; Eitner 1971, 52, fig. 4; Eitner 1972, 153, no. 33, pl. 27; Hamilton-New York-Amsterdam 1985/86, fig. 25

Exhibitions: Berkeley 1968, no. 84; Los Angeles-Detroit-Philadelphia 1971/72, no. 76; Providence 1975, no. 75

Stanford, Stanford University Museum of Art, gift of the Committee for Art at Stanford. Inv. no. 67.50

In this drawing, Géricault isolated the central group of fallen angels in Jonas Suyderhoef's engraving of 1642 after Rubens's *Small Last Judgement* in the Staatliche Graphische Sammlung, Munich (Fig. 55–1) to explore the expressive, contorted poses and the complex interweaving of the tumbling figures. He carefully delineated the clear outlines and hatchings of the engraving and adopted its composition which reverses that of the original.

Géricault used figures from this copy and others after Suyderhoef's print in preliminary sketches for his revolutionary painting of 1819 *The Raft of the Medusa* (Musée du Louvre).[1] Early preparatory drawings in Amsterdam and Rouen show how Géricault adapted the scene from the Last Judgement to the drama of mutiny at sea.[2] Géricault ultimately discarded the initial theme of mutiny as the subject matter for the painting, but the shrouded cadaver trailing the raft and the kneeling figure at the centre of the finished painting still are directly related to Suyderhoef's engraving.[3] Furthermore, the heroic physiques of the starved survivors and the tangled massing of their bodies abroad the raft derive in a general manner from Rubens's model. Géricault's reference to the Fall of the Damned elevated the horrific depiction of a contemporary event to the level of monumental history painting as if creating a profane Last Judgement.[4]

P.V.

1   A similar sheet by Géricault in the Pierre Dubaut Collection, Paris, reproduces two other groups from the print by Suyderhoef: *Groupes d'une chute des damnés*, see Eitner 1971, 53, fig. 6. Additional copies by Géricault are known indirectly through drawings by Delacroix after Géricault. *Dessins d'après Géricault* (Collection A. Doria, Paris) *Croquis d'après une étude de Géricault.* (Collection Lee Diamondstein, New York). See Eitner 1971, 53, fig. 7 and 54, figs. 8–9.

2   For example, *La Révolte des matelots*, (Gemeentemusea, Amsterdam), see Eitner 1971, 54, fig. 12.

3   For a preliminary sketch for the kneeling figure, *Figure Studies: Sketch of a Kneeling Man* (Private Collection), see Eitner 1972, no. 58, pl. 52. The figure of the trailing cadaver was only added after the completion of the painting, just prior to its exhibition. A sketch for the shrouded cadaver is included at the lower right of *Five Sketches of a Nude Lying on his Back* (Delestre Collection, Paris), see Eitner 1972, 163, no. 77, pl. 76.

4   Although Jean Jouvenet's *Triumph of Justice* has been cited as a primary influence on Géricault's *The Raft of the Medusa*, especially in similarities in isolated figures, it appears more likely that both artists copied and adapted Suyderhoef's engraving. See Knowlton 1942, 125–144.

55 Fall of the Rebel Angels

Fig 55-1 Jonas Suyderhoef after Sir Peter Paul Rubens *The Fall of Lucifer*, (detail). Stanford University Museum of Art, Mortimer C. Leventritt Fund, Stanford

56 Sheet of Studies

Eugène Delacroix

Charenton-Saint-Maurice 1798–Paris 1863

56 Sheet of Studies
From Dürer

Pencil and brush and brown ink
195 × 150 mm
Inscribed upper centre: *page 101* [*?*]/*2e vol*/*une autre figure*/*envelopée*
[*?*]; and centre right: *2e vol*/*Page 117* [*?*]
Provenance: Vente Delacroix (L. 838a); P. Burty; H. Rouart;
L. Rouart; M. Feilchenfeldt
Bibliography: Moreau 1873, 130; Robaut 1885, no. 777;
Escholier 1926–29, I, 241; Mende 1971, XLIII, fig. 23;
Ganeval 1976, 44
Exhibitions: Bern 1963, no. 187; Bremen 1964, no. 272;
Tübingen-Brussels 1986, no. 163

Private Collection

In his Journal (10 March 1849), Delacroix praised Dürer for
his ability to render all aspects of nature with equal perfection.
He also studied his woodcuts in connection with his illustrations
to Goethe's *Götz von Berlichingen* (1836–43).[1] Among Delacroix's
drawings after Dürer, this sheet is unusual for he added to the
details copied from woodcuts a sketch after Dürer's *Self-Portrait*
of 1498 (Prado, Madrid). The image reverses the painting so
Delacroix must have copied it from a print (Fig. 56–1).[2] Using
brush and brown ink for the background and some details,
Delacroix appropriated a technique Dürer had employed in
some of his drawings to give greater relief to the figures.[3]
Moreover, he transformed Dürer's likeness and headgear giving
him the appearance of an Arab. Thus he associated the German
master with the people who represented for him a living legacy
of an ideal classical past.

The pencil sketches in the margins represent figures and
objects from five different woodcuts that must have been bound
together at the time Delacroix copied them.[4] The figure of the
torturer at upper left from *The Martyrdom of St. John the Evangelist*
(B. 61) Delacroix also endowed with more of an oriental quality.
The figure of St. George at upper right (from B. 111) is similar
to other copies of men in armour Delacroix made after the woodcuts of Cranach, Burgkmair, Beham, and Flötner.[5] While the
graphic work of these sixteenth-century artists had long been the
traditional source in the training of young artists, Delacroix's
quick, calligraphic rendering of the motifs suggests that he was
less interested in perfecting a linear technique for his woodcuts
than in finding an archetypal medieval German figure and
objects.

The distribution of motifs on this sheet, the pencil sketches
surrounding the portrait at centre, recalls one of Delacroix's
lithographic illustrations to Goethe's *Faust* (1828) and may be
related as well to Peter Cornelius's illustrations to *Faust* (1809).[6]
In this work, the text page is surrounded by illustrations in the
margin. Cornelius had adopted this format from Nepomuk Strix-
ner's facsimile of Dürer's marginal decorations for the prayer-
book of Emperor Maximilian (1808) which Goethe himself
recommended to him for inspiration. Delacroix knew Cornelius's
work and may have consciously adapted it to this drawing.[7]

The study of Dürer's woodcuts provided Delacroix with a
vocabulary of figures and forms that could evoke both the German and classical past. By referring to the sixteenth-century
works, Delacroix participated in the 'Dürer-revival' fostered by
writers and artists, particularly the Nazarenes, during the first
half of the nineteenth century.[8]
C.L.

Fig 56-1 Wenceslaus Hollar after Albrecht Dürer *Self-Portrait*. Staatliche
Museen Preussischer Kulturbesitz, Kupferstichkabinett, Berlin

1   Joubin 1932, I, 273 and Robaut 1885, no. 777. For a general discussion
of Delacroix and Goethe, see Jamot 1932, 279–298 and Busch 1973.
2   The print after Dürer by Wenceslaus Hollar is mentioned and illustrated
in Anzelewsky 1971, 152–155, no. 49 and fig. 33.
3   Discussed and reproduced in Winkler 1937, II, nos. 355, 422, 424, 427,
and 428.
4   Delacroix copied details from the woodcuts: *The Last Supper* (B. 53),
The Martyrdom of St. John the Evangelist (B. 61), *St. George killing the Dragon*
(B. 111), *St. Jerome in his Cell* (B. 114), and *The Head of St. John the Baptist
brought to Herodius* (B. 126). That a book might be the source for this sheet
is suggested by the inscriptions.
5   See Ganeval 1976, 40–48.
6   Delacroix's lithograph, *Mephistopheles introducing himself to Martha*, first
state, is illustrated in Trapp 1971, 148, fig. 75; one of Cornelius's is discussed
and illustrated in Andrews 1964, 31, fig. 23a.
7   Trapp 1971, 144.
8   On the 'Dürer-revival' see Lüdecke and Heiland 1955.

57 The Deposition

Eugène Delacroix

Charenton-Saint-Maurice 1798–Paris 1863

57 The Deposition
From Rubens's altarpiece

Pen and brown ink
322 × 211 mm
Provenance: F. Koenigs
Bibliography: Hoetink 1968, no. 103 (with further references)
Exhibitions: Previous to 1964 listed in Hoetink 1968, no. 103;
  Bremen 1964, no. 249; Tübingen-Brussels 1986, no. 156

Rotterdam, Museum Boymans-van Beuningen. Inv. no. F II 84

Heir to Rubens's colourism, Delacroix made numerous drawings after the Flemish master which demonstrate he inherited much more. The beauty of this drawing lies in the vigorous quality of the penwork so well suited to the pathos of the subject matter and clearly inspired by Rubens's lively brushstroke. Delacroix knew Rubens's *Descent from the Cross* in the Cathedral of Antwerp from a print; a sheet of studies from 1835 reproduces some of the subsidiary figures in reverse.[1] But the present drawing follows the direction of the original composition (Fig. 57–1) and has none of the controlled lines of the detail study which echo the character of the print. Delacroix may have copied either directly or from memory the original in Antwerp where he travelled twice, in 1839 and 1850.[2]

Delacroix made a number of changes to the model. He conceived of the figure of Christ in a single plane and so introduced distortion to the anatomy where it is foreshortened in Rubens's painting, as in the right forearm. Furthermore, he reduced the strong compositional diagonal by altering the left arm and eliminating the shroud used to lower Christ. By substituting a loincloth for the shroud, he bared Christ's left leg and thus imagined what it looked like under the veil, endowing it with the imprint of his own hand. Other artists had done this before him and so Delacroix participated in a practice which reflects the similar interests and training of artists over the centuries.[3]

Delacroix had a profound interest in and admiration for Rubens's religious scenes. Often he used sketches such as this one as a source of motifs. In creating the figure of Christ for his *Pietà* of 1850 in the Nasjonalgalleriet, Oslo, he must have used his copy of Rubens's *Le Christ à la paille* in the Antwerp Museum.[4] But there are no later reflections of this drawing, indeed he never painted a Deposition.
  C.L.

Fig 57-1 Sir Peter Paul Rubens *Descent from the Cross*. Cathedral of Antwerp

1   See London 1964, no. 136, fig. 74.
2   The drawing has been dated to 1839 by Hoetink following von Heusinger in Bremen 1964, no. 249.
3   See Jaffé 1977, 25, pl. 23.
4   Delacroix's drawing (Musée du Louvre, inv. no. RF 10484) is reproduced in Sérullaz 1984, II, no. 1349; Rubens's painting in Oldenbourg 1921, 160; and Delacroix's painting in Johnson 1986, III, no. 443, IV, pl. 255.

58 A mounted Arab attacking a Panther

Eugène Delacroix

Charenton-Saint-Maurice 1798–Paris 1863

58 A mounted Arab attacking a Panther
From Pieter Soutman's etching after Rubens

Graphite pencil
240 × 204 mm
Provenance: Delacroix Family; D. Darcy (L. Suppl. 652 f.);
    Cailac; M. Gobin; M. and P.J. Sachs
Bibliography: Mongan and Sachs 1940, I, no. 683, fig. 356
Exhibitions: Cambridge 1955, no. 4; New York 1958/59,
    no. 116; Minneapolis etc. 1962, no. 32; Paris 1963 (I),
    no. 463; Paris 1963 (II), no. 465 (with further references);
    Cambridge 1965, no. 48; Providence 1975, no. 85;
    Tübingen-Brussels 1986, no. 156

Cambridge, Harvard University Art Museums (Fogg Art Mus-
    eum), Bequest of Meta and Paul J. Sachs. Inv. no. 1965.268

With minimal means, Delacroix captured in this quick sketch
all the activity and emotional power of Rubens's *Hippopotamus
Hunt* (Alte Pinakothek, Munich) known to him in the etching
by Soutman (Fig. 58–1).[1] Focussing only on Arab, horse, and
beast, he suggested both volume and movement with multiple
contour lines. By varying the quality of these lines, he distinguished the heroism of the hunter from the fear of his steed.
Delacroix introduced shading to the hunter's face and arm alone
and so conveyed his concentration and effort. By including the
turban and the bare feet, Delacroix emphasized the exotic character of the Arab and thus referred in his own way to the classical
past that once had drawn Rubens to the theme of the hunt.[2]

The figural group bears some resemblance to that in
Delacroix's painting of 1849, *Arab on Horseback attacked by a Lion*
(Art Institute of Chicago) but it is not a preparatory study.[3]
Indeed, he used none of his numerous copies after Rubens's
Hunts as studies for his paintings.[4] Rather, the drawing dem-
onstrates the general manner in which Delacroix benefitted from
Rubens in his effort to arrive at his own definition of the romantic
conflict between man and the forces of nature.[5]

    C.L.

Fig 58-1 Pieter Soutman *after* Peter Paul Rubens *Hippopotamus Hunt*. The
Metropolitan Museum of Art, New York

1   See Balis 1986, 120, no. 5, copy 14, fig. 49.
2   On Delacroix and Orientalism, see Stevens 1984, 19, 124, no. 18.
3   The painting is reproduced in Johnson 1986, III, no. 181, IV, pl. 13.
Johnson believes a drawing in the Fogg, reproduced in Mongan and Sachs
1940, III, fig. 358, is a study for the painting. Following Sérullaz, he believes
this drawing is the *première pensée* for the *Tiger Hunt* of 1854 (Musée du Louvre)
mentioned in Delacroix's *Journal*, see Joubin 1952, II, 224, and Johnson
1986, III, no. 194, IV, pl. 21. See also Providence 1975, no. 85.
4   For other studies in the Louvre after Rubens's Hunts, see Sérullaz 1984,
II, nos. 1752 folio 12v, 13r, 14r, 17r, 18r, and 1753 folio 8v, 9r and v, 10r,
11r, 12r.
5   On the difference between Delacroix's and Rubens's conceptions of
man's relation to nature, see Kliman 1982, 446–466.

59 Two Figures from the 'Judgement of Paris'

Eugène Delacroix

Charenton-Saint-Maurice 1798–Paris 1863

59 Two Figures from the 'Judgement of Paris'
From Marcantonio Raimondi's engraving after Raphael

Pencil
    184 × 194 mm
Provenance: Vente Delacroix (L. 838a); Schaeffer Galleries;
    Sale, Galerie Kornfeld, Bern, 19–20 June 1985, no. 161;
    Sale, C.G. Boerner, Düsseldorf, 6–17 May 1986, no. 52, repr.
Bibliography: Lichtenstein 1977, 503–504, fig. 41

New York, Jill Newhouse and Eric Carlson

The attention focussed recently on Delacroix's drawings after
Raphael has dispelled, to a certain extent, his reputation as the
great 'Rubéniste'.[1] The drawings differ markedly from his copies
after Rubens being, in general, highly controlled and meticulously rendered. In his study of Marcantonio's engraving after
Raphael's lost drawing, the *Judgement of Paris* (Fig. 59–1),
Delacroix isolated two figures from different parts of the composition, a naiad and a river god, and sought to reproduce their
sinuous and complex poses without distortion to their anatomy.
Following Géricault's practice (Cat. no. 55), Delacroix first
outlined the contours, making corrections as needed to the
naiad's back, knee and calf, and then shaded the figures with
strokes approximating the hatching of the engraving. For all his
attention to detail, Delacroix introduced a greater sense of
naturalism particularly to the river god. Its musculature is less
geometrized and its physiognomy less correct, but the figure conveys a greater sense of langour and psychological presence.

Delacroix copied elements of Marcantonio's engraving in
two other sheets now in Besançon.[2] One bears a clumsy rendering of the river god and the personification of victory, the second
reproduces the figures exactly as they appear in this drawing.
They are not in equal proportion to one another, however, nor
are they as anatomically convincing, so this study probably preceded the one shown here. Considered together, these copies
illustrate Delacroix's desire and concerted effort to master and
improve upon the graceful poses of Raphael's mythological
figures.

This drawing has been dated by Lichtenstein to *c.* 1840.[3]
Certainly it must connect with the monumental cycle of mural
paintings of 1833–47 which Delacroix executed for the Palais
Bourbon.[4] The Raphaelesque figures differ considerably from
those in his earlier works. This study shows us that Delacroix
looked to Raphael as a source of classical figure types as Rubens
did before him.[5]

For another copy after Marcantonio's engraving of the
Judgement of Paris, see the next entry.
    C.L.

Fig 59-1 Marcantonio Raimondi after Raphael *Judgement of Paris*.
Rijksprentenkabinet, Amsterdam

1   Lichtenstein 1971, pp. 525–533, 593–603.
2   Lichtenstein 1971, nos. 24 and 25, figs. 35 and 36.
3   Lichtenstein 1977, 503.
4   On Delacroix's mural paintings, see Sérullaz 1963.
5   See Jaffé 1977, 22–29.

60 Figures from the 'Parnassus' and 'Judgement of Paris'

Edgar Degas

Paris 1834–1917

60 Figures from the 'Parnassus' and 'Judgement of Paris'

From Marcantonio Raimondi's engravings after Raphael

Pen and brown ink on cream tracing paper; laid down
317 × 152 mm
Provenance: Fèvre collection

Fig 60-1 Marcantonio Raimondi after Raphael *Parnassus*. Rijksprentenkabinet, Amsterdam

Fig 60-2 Marcantonio Raimondi after Raphael *Judgement of Paris*. Rijksprentenkabinet, Amsterdam

Bibliography: Reff 1963, 241, 151, fig. 1; Russoli and Minervino 1970, fig. 2
Exhibitions: Cambridge 1961, no. 12; St. Louis-Philadelphia-Minneapolis 1967, 36, 38, no. 13; London 1971 (I), no. 123; Paris 1983/84, 98, no. 62, fig. 170

Cambridge, Harvard University Art Museums (Fogg Art Museum), Anonymous gift in memory of W.G. Russell Allen. Inv. no. 1956.10

In this drawing, Degas has taken details from two engravings by Marcantonio Raimondi after Raphael: the *Parnassus* (B. XIV.200-01.247) which records Raphael's early design for his fresco in the Vatican, and the *Judgement of Paris* (B. XIV.197.245), after a lost work of Raphael. Degas copied the seated Calliope and the group of the three arch-poets, Dante, Homer with his scribe, and Virgil from the *Parnassus* (Fig. 60–1) and the two river gods from the *Judgement of Paris* (Fig. 60–2).[1] The study of the head at the corner has not been connected with any engraving.

Degas copied from reproductive engravings during his short time at the Ecole des Beaux-Arts and while training with Lamothe before his trip to Italy.[2] Here he used tracing paper, probably tracing the outlines of the figures from the prints and then adding parallel lines of shading. Degas often preferred tracing paper when he wished to vary a design in subsequent stages, by tracing and altering, and repeating the process, a technique Ingres had also employed. Degas started with one detail, shifted the paper in order to find a blank area, and traced another section without regard to their relation to each other.

It is not only the images but also the precision of the engraved line which Degas wished to record. In certain areas, such as the drapery folds of the Homer group, the drawn parallel lines of shading are not as extensive as in the print. In other areas, though, such as the oak-leaf wreath of the river god who faces out, Degas softened the precise engraved line and in doing so, made this figure seem more lively.

In Cat. no. 59, Delacroix copied the *Judgement of Paris*; Cat. no. 28 illustrates Poussin's interpretation of Raphael's *Parnassus*.[3]

J.C.

1   From the engraving after *Parnassus*, Degas has also included a tree and an outline study of the right leg of Calliope. The river gods from the *Judgement of Paris* also inspired Manet in his *Déjeuner sur l'herbe* (Musée d'Orsay, Paris).
2   Degas's notebooks, especially the earlier one from 1853–56, contain numerous copies of engravings. See index in Reff 1976 (II), for a complete listing. Reff has also been able to identify many of the sources of Degas's single sheets, see his articles in *Burlington Magazine*, especially Reff 1964 (II), 258, where he lists eight drawings from a private collection in Paris as being inspired by Marcantonio's engravings after Raphael, including another of the *Judgement of Paris*.
3   For other examples of copies after the *Judgement of Paris* and *Parnassus*, see Paris 1983/84, 423–425 and 349–352.

61 The Battle of San Romano

Edgar Degas

Paris 1834–1917

61 The Battle of San Romano
After Paolo Uccello

Pencil
245 × 392 mm
Annotated at upper left: *Florence 1859/Paolo Uccello*
Provenance: Degas Sale, Galerie Georges Petit, Paris, IVème
vente, 2–4 July, 1919, no. 92b, repr.; C. Vignier; Sale, Parke
Bernet, New York, March 1963
Bibliography: Walker 1933, 185; Vitali 1963, 269 n. 6; Reff 1964
(II), 251 n. 16; Russoli and Minervino 1970, no. 21
Exhibitions: Tübingen-Berlin 1984, no. 36; Rome 1984/85,
no. 18

Zürich, Private collection

Degas copied from Paolo Uccello's painting, *The Unhorsing of
Bernardino della Carda*, in the Uffizi, Florence, the centre panel
of the set of three scenes, *The Battle of San Romano*, commissioned
in 1456 (Fig. 61–1).[1] Degas only lightly sketched the background landscape, almost black in the painting, and concentrated on the many figures and horses in the foreground. This
is one of the very few instances in which he copied an entire composition. Usually he extracted a single detail for study, as in his
copies after other early Italian artists, Botticelli, Ghirlandaio,
Gozzoli, and Signorelli, as well as Uccello, which he made during
his travels in Italy between 1854 and 1859.[2]

The early historical subjects Degas painted upon his return
to Paris, *The Daughter of Jephthah* (Smith College Museum of Art,
Northampton) and *Semiramis Constructing a Town* (Musée du
Louvre, Paris) were strongly dependent on his researches into
the art of the past.[3] Among the studies he made for these paintings are numerous copies after artists such as Dürer, Mantegna,
Delacroix, and even Mughal miniatures from which he borrowed details or motifs for his finished works. Neither of these
early paintings incorporate specific elements from his copy after
Uccello. But the archaizing manner in which Degas disposed the
horses and groups of figures across a proscenium-like setting in
these two paintings may have been suggested to him by Uccello's
model.

Degas also copied horses from the work of artists such as
Delacroix, Géricault, various English horse painters, as well as
from casts of the Parthenon frieze. The present copy may be seen
as an early instance of Degas's life-long fascination with horses
and riders that is manifest in his works in all media throughout
his career.
　　J.C.

Fig 61-1 Paolo Uccello *The Battle of San Romano*. Uffizi, Florence

1   Pope-Hennessy 1969, 17–21, pl. 61. Cosimo de Medici commissioned
Paolo Uccello to paint this set to commemorate the Battle of San Romano
fought on 1 June 1432. The other two panels are *Niccolò da Tolentino directing
the Battle of San Romano* (National Gallery, London) and *Micheletto da Cotignola
attacking the Sienese from the Rear* (Musée du Louvre, Paris).
2   See Reff 1976 (II), notebook 12, 89 and notebook 12, 3; Reff is unsure
if this is after the equestrian portrait of Niccolò da Tolentino by Castagno
of 1456 or Uccello's portrait of Sir John Hawkwood of 1436, both in the
Duomo of Florence.
3   See Lemoisne 1946, nos. 94 and 83. A connection between the painting
of *Semiramis* and details from the works of Mantegna and Delacroix both
of whom Degas was copying at this time, has been established (Reff 1963,
242 and Fries 1964, 355).

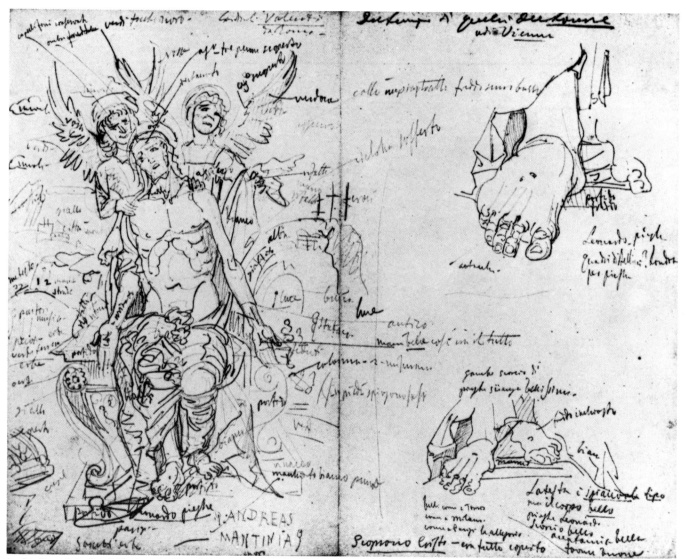

62 Studies of the Dead Christ with Two Angels

Giovanni Battista Cavalcaselle

Verona 1819–Rome 1897

62 Studies of the Dead Christ with Two Angels
From Andrea Mantegna

Pen and ink
225 × 286 mm
Exhibition: Venice 1973, 64

Venice, Biblioteca Nazionale Marciana. Inv. no. Cod. Marc. It.
IV, 2033, fasc. 7

Giovanni Battista Cavalcaselle and his literary partner, Joseph
Arthur Crowe, helped shape art history as we know it. They
combined archival research, connoisseurship, and social and
political history in an unprecedented fashion. The results were
a series of sound reconstructions of artists' personalities brilliantly
and firmly set in their cultural contexts. Among nineteenth-
century critics of the arts, only Burckhardt, Berenson, and Warburg have had a greater influence on later generations of Renaissance scholars.

Crowe and Cavalcaselle's partnership began with a chance
meeting on a train in 1847.[1] They published their first work
together, *The Early Flemish Painters*, in 1856. Other multi-volume
series soon followed: *The History of Painting in Italy*, 1864–1866,
and in 1871, *A History of Painting in North Italy*. In 1877 they published their study of Titian and in 1882, their life of Raphael.
The Life and Times of Titian is still generally considered the finest
and most thorough work every produced on the artist.

Although both Crowe and Cavalcaselle had been trained
as painters, Cavalcaselle had the finer eye and his lot was to con-
centrate on connoisseurship. Crowe did the historical research
and wrote every word of their joint efforts. As a connoisseur,
Cavalcaselle has been greatly praised for his diligence, perspi-
cacity, and prodigious memory. He shunned the use of photographs. Instead, as *aides-mémoire* he made drawings of every
painting he intended to write about. Cavalcaselle's approach to
studying paintings by means of visual and written notes was sys-
tematic. He first made a rapid and light sketch of the monument
which he then reworked in a darker tint to emphasize the
singular or tell-tale qualities of the picture. At this point, he often
made studies of details as well. Finally, he added colour-notes
and remarks on the state of preservation. As Pope-Hennessy has
pointed out, Cavalcaselle chose extremely vivid and precise
terms for colours, such as *castagno*, *cioccolato*, and *caffè*.[2] Other
nineteenth-century art historians, such as Morelli, Burckhardt,
and Wölfflin, also used drawings to learn the styles of artists.
But none of them copied works as assiduously and systematically
as Cavalcaselle. There are literally hundreds of his drawings preserved at the Biblioteca Marciana.

The drawing here exhibited Cavalcaselle made in Copenhagen in 1865 during his trip to Northern Europe to carry out
research for *A History of Painting in North Italy*. One can see clearly
characteristic elements of Cavalcaselle's style of recording
impressions. The reinforced lines, for example, stress the physical
eccentricities of Mantegna's Christ (Fig. 62–1): his heroic and
classicistic torso topped by lean shoulders and flanked by thin
arms. Cavalcaselle's notes include the comments, 'La testa è spia-

cevole tipo, ma il corpo bello, pieghe Leonardo, . . . anatomia
bella, forma buona'.[3] In Crowe's words in 1871, these notes
became:

> A splendid exhibition of skill in the reproduction of nude
> and accessorial detail, but too realistic [in grief stricken
> expression] to produce absolute pleasure . . . We know of no
> picture of the master in which form is given with more purity,
> drapery with more studied art, and chiaroscuro with more
> Leonardesque perfection.[4]

A.B.

Fig 62-1 Andrea Mantegna *The Dead Christ Between Two Angels*. Statens
Museum for Kunst, Copenhagen

1   The most readable account of the lives of Crowe and Cavalcaselle is
Langton Douglas's introduction to Crowe and Cavalcaselle 1923, I, ix–xvii.
For Cavalcaselle, see also *Dizionario* 1979, with further references.
2   Pope-Hennessy 1980, 13.
3   These are comments cited in Venice 1973, 64. Translated they mean,
'The head is a displeasing type, but the body is beautiful, folds Leonardo,
. . . anatomy beautiful, form good.'
4   Crowe and Cavalcaselle 1871, I, 403.

63 Christ on the Cross

Paul Cézanne

Aix-en-Provence 1839–1906

63 Christ on the Cross
From van Dyck

Pencil on laid paper
300 × 210 mm
Provenance: P. Cézanne fils; J.-P. Cézanne
Bibliography: Venturi 1936, no. 1220 [1879–90]; Berthold
     1958, no. 228; Chappuis 1973, no. 311 [1873–76]
Exhibitions: Newcastle upon Tyne-London 1973, no. 21;
     Tübingen 1978, no. 161

Zürich, Marianne Feilchenfeldt

Focussing solely upon the figure of Christ in van Dyck's *Christ on the Cross, The Virgin Mary, St. John and Mary Magdalene* in the Louvre (Fig. 63–1), Cézanne studied the human form as though he were drawing from life.[1] Only faint indications of the mountainous background, the Magdalene's hands, and the Cross allude to the source. Cézanne eliminated all signs of the Passion, reduced the contrapposto of Christ's pose, and thus suggested little of the pathos of van Dyck's painting. Instead, he delineated a figure at once more adolescent and possessing calm monumentality.

The figure in the drawing is similar to *The Bather* of *c.* 1885 (Museum of Modern Art, New York).[2] Both are isolated, seminude, and frontal, with bowed head and left leg brought forward. Lacking proper live models, Cézanne often copied in the Louvre depending on the old masters for examples of anatomical modelling and expressive pose. Furthermore, he alluded to older images in his depictions of bathers in order to elevate this secular non-narrative theme to the level of mythological and historical painting. But the male bather of the type standing frontally is now known to derive from a photograph of a live model.[3] Thus the present drawing may be seen as an independent variation on the motif, dependent on the older image of Christ.

The *Christ on the Cross* was attributed to Rubens at the time when Cézanne copied it.[4] Cézanne claimed Rubens was his favourite painter and made numerous drawings after the master's works in Paris.[5] The model Cézanne chose here, however, is unusual for he generally favoured – as Delacroix did – more robustly modelled figures such as the Naiads, Bellona, and the Victory from the paintings in the Medici cycle. Though he most often employed sculpture for study, the voluminous forms of Rubens's figures served him well as a means to experiment with his innovative method of planar facetting.

    C.L.

Fig 63-1 Anthony van Dyck *Christ on the Cross, The Virgin Mary, St. John and Mary Magdalene*. Musée du Louvre, Paris

1   For a study of Cézanne and his artistic models, see Berthold 1958.
2   Barr 1954, 23, repr.
3   Barr 1954, 22 and Reff 1960.
4   The painting formerly attributed to Rubens was only recently given to van Dyck and is dated to the time he was painting in Rubens's studio, see Brejon de Lavergnée et al. 1979, inv. 1766.
5   See Chappuis 1973, I, 26.

64 Study of a Monument

Paul Cézanne

Aix-en-Provence 1839–1906

64 Study of a Monument
Pencil, pen and India ink, and watercolour
217 × 126 mm

Verso: *Landscape at the Jas de Bouffon*, and *Portrait of a Young Man, after Bacchiacca*

Provenance: P. Cézanne fils; P. Cassirer; F. Koenigs (L. 1023a)

Bibliography: Venturi 1936, no. 870 [1879–85]; Berthold 1958, 154; Hoetink 1968, no. 29; Rewald 1983, no. 64 [1878–80] (with further references)

Exhibitions: Rotterdam 1933/34, no. 12; Amsterdam 1938, no. 3; Tübingen-Zürich 1982, no. 105

Rotterdam, Museum Boymans-van Beuningen. Inv. no. F II 211

Although Cézanne preferred pencil, he also made watercolour drawings after works of art. Unlike the pencil copies, which are usually detail studies, the watercolours render the examples completely. Many of these are on leaves from sketchbooks, so while they are self-contained works of art, Cézanne did not intend them to be *murables*.[1] Probably Cézanne sought to add another dimension to the pictorial scaffolding he laid down in pencil by using colour to suggest volume and atmosphere. Just as he tended to geometrize forms in his pencil studies, by putting down colour in discrete layers he dissected the sculpture into semi-independent parts.

The figure in this study of a monument is difficult to read; its source has not been identified. Most likely, it represents a donor figure from a funerary monument, who prays and kneels before his coat of arms. Cézanne could have encountered such a statue among the casts in the Trocadero, in the collection of Zola, or among the numerous reproductions in his possession.[2] If indeed the drawing is after a funerary monument in bronze, or even a cast, then his addition of colour is all the more surprising.

Just as landscape is a genre seldom copied by artists, so too is watercolour a medium rarely employed to interpret or learn from the past.[3] Only in the early twentieth century, with the autonomy of colour and the new decorative tendencies that emerged, especially in French artistic circles, did artists such as de la Fresnaye and Dufy (Cat. no. 70) employ watercolour for copies in which they would superimpose their own styles on works from the past.[4]

C.L.

1   For other watercolour copies, see Rewald 1983, nos. 65, 67, 145, 297, 492, 556–560.
2   Two pencil drawings of the head and shoulders alone are in the same sketchbook, one on the same sheet as a portrait of Zola, see Chappuis 1973, no. 626 and 625. The watercolour belongs to a different sketchbook.
3   On copies in watercolour, see the brief comments made in Koschatzky 1970, 55 and 61.
4   For watercolour copies by de la Fresnaye, see Seligman 1969, nos. 426–428.

65 The rebellious Slave

Paul Cézanne

Aix-en-Provence 1839–1906

65 The rebellious Slave
After Michelangelo's sculpture

Graphite pencil
447 × 295 mm
Provenance: Bernheim-Jeune; Galerie Thannhauser; P. Lamb;
 C. Valentin; J.S. Newberry
Bibliography: Venturi 1936, no. 1443 [1879–82]; Berthold
 1958, 58; Chappuis 1973, no. 679 [1885–88] (with further
 references)
Exhibitions: Washington-Chicago-Boston 1971, no. 76

Detroit, The Detroit Institute of Arts, Bequest of John S. Newberry. Inv. no. 65.140

Cézanne never travelled to Italy but knew the work of
Michelangelo first-hand from the two *Slaves* in the Louvre. He
made numerous copies of each, both *in situ* and from a photograph he owned of the *Bound Captive*. In this study, Cézanne
copied the sculpture itself (Fig. 65–1) including the column that
once stood behind it in the Michelangelo room of the Louvre.[1]
He lightly delineated the figure and interlocked it with its setting
by merging its contours with those of the column behind. The
strongly defined musculature of the sculpture he indicated in an
abbreviated fashion with geometric facets. This so-called 'constructive stroke' Cézanne also used to model form in many of
his copies after the plaster cast he owned of an *écorché* figure then
attributed to Michelangelo.[2] Later in life, in a letter to Camoin,
Cézanne characterized Michelangelo as 'un constructeur'.[3]

 Cézanne never made use of the pose of the *Rebellious Slave*
as he did with the *Dying Slave*, incorporating it into his paintings
of male bathers. Reff has suggested that this pose may have had
tragi-erotic associations for Cézanne.[4] Certainly, the three-
quarter angle from which Cézanne elected to draw the *Rebellious
Slave* deemphasizes its power in favour of sensuousness.

 The muscularity and contorted postures of Michelangelo's
Slaves have long attracted the attention of artists. Degas copied
the *Dying Slave* in a pencil drawing to explore the fall of light
and shade on the sculpture much as Tintoretto did in his own
way in his copies of casts after Michelangelo's sculptures (Cat.
no. 10).[5] Cézanne stands apart, however, in focussing on the possibilities of geometrizing forms with a minimum of attention to
chiaroscuro.
 C.L.

1 See Chappuis 1973, nos. 375, 473, 678, and 1208 for drawings after the
Dying Slave and Chappuis nos. 303, 589, and 590 for drawings after the *Rebellious Slave*. On Cézanne's photograph, see Reff 1960, 304, no. 4; through
the references he gives us for the *Dying Slave*. For a photograph of the
Michelangelo Room, see Chappuis 1973, I, fig. 42.
2 For a reproduction of the *écorché*, see Chappuis 1973, I, 101, fig. 36 and
nos. 565–74, 980, and 1086–89, especially 556, 568, and 574 for Cézanne's
copies after it. On Cézanne's constructive stroke, see Reff 1962, 214–227.
3 Rewald 1937, 267–268.
4 See Reff 1959, 26–29, 68.
5 The drawing by Degas is in the collection of Marianne Feilchenfeldt,
Zürich and reproduced in Tübingen-Berlin 1984, no. 39.

Fig 65-1 Michelangelo Buonarroti *Rebellious Slave*. Musée du Louvre, Paris

66 Personages of Goya

James Ensor

Ostend 1860–1949

66 Personages of Goya

After Goya's Capricho no. 51, *Se repulen*

Pencil
 157 × 226 mm
Inscribed lower left: *après Goya/c'est un si grand inconvénient d'avoir
les ongles trop longs que cela est défendu même dans la sorcellerie*
Provenance: J.W. Alsdorf
Exhibition: Chicago-New York 1976, no. 69

Chicago, The Art Institute of Chicago, Gift of Mr. and Mrs.
 James W. Alsdorf. Inv. no. 1965.1184

Ensor copied the work of Goya not to develop technical expertise
nor as a stylistic exercise but because he was attracted to its
bizarre subject matter. Indeed, he must have felt an affinity for
Goya's view of man and society as he expressed it through the
use of masquerade or the supernatural in his work. In the drawing of Capricho no. 51, *Se repulen* ('They spruce themselves up')
(Fig. 66–1), Ensor changed the format from vertical to horizontal but retained all elements of the composition.[1] Below he
inscribed a French translation of Goya's Spanish commentary:
'This business of having long nails is so pernicious that even
among witches it is forbidden'. Even if Ensor may not have associated long nails with voraciousness and therefore may not have
recognized Goya's satire on the theme of greed, he would have
been fascinated – as we are – by the grotesque figures and the
irrational incident depicted.[2]

While the masks from his mother's shop suggested a powerful
pictorial vocabulary to him, Ensor also drew from the work of
socially conscious artists. He copied Callot, Daumier, Rowland-
son, and Gillray, among others.[3] Ensor never incorporated their
satirical caricatures into his own imagery, but through the process of copying (often from photographs), primarily during his
first years back in Ostend after quitting the Brussels academy
in 1880, Ensor became thoroughly versed in the devices of social
satire.

With the growing symbolist concern for the fantastic and
the suggestive in the 1880s, Goya attained popularity, especially
amongst printmakers. Odilon Redon made a series of
lithographs entitled 'Hommage à Goya' and Klinger acknowledged Goya as well.[4] Delacroix preceded them, in a different
vein (and in a different medium). He wrote of his idea to draw
caricatures in the style of Goya in 1824 and he made several
drawings after motifs from the *Caprichos*.[5]
    C.L.

Fig 66–1 Francisco de Goya *Se repulen*. Plate 51 of 80 from 'Los Caprichos',
1799. National Gallery of Art, Washington, Rosenwald Collection

---

1   Probably Ensor had a reversed print at his disposal.
2   For an interpretative discussion of the Capricho no. 51, see Lopez-Rey
1953, I, 144.
3   See Schoonbaert 1972 and Schoonbaert 1968, 311–342.
4   On the critical history of Goya, see Glendinning 1977.
5   For reproductions and a discussion of Delacroix's Goya, see Sérullaz,
1980/81.

67 The Abduction of Rebecca

Henri Matisse

Le Cateau-Cambrésis 1869–Nice 1954

67 The Abduction of Rebecca
After Delacroix

Pen and ink
    262 × 187 mm
Inscribed and signed lower right: *D'après E.D. – Henri Matisse*;
    and signed lower left: *Henri Matisse*
Provenance: W.M. Ivens; Sale, Parke Bernet, New York, 11
    January 1963
Bibliography: *Art News* 1963, 9, repr.; Cowart 1972, 148 n. 18,
    fig. 101 [1903/04]; Jacobus 1972, 18. fig. 10; Bock 1981, 16

New York, William E. OReilly

In this lively pen and ink drawing, Matisse reinterprets the interplay of light and shade in Delacroix's painting of a scene from
Sir Walter Scott's *Ivanhoe* (Fig. 67–1). Matisse's calligraphic
penwork indicates his affinity for van Gogh's drawings, two of
which he owned.[1] His use of the white of the paper to suggest
the fall of light on the forms recalls Delacroix's drawings. Both
the definition of volume and the bold expressive line of the
present drawing presage the early Fauve paintings Matisse made
in 1905 at Collioure.[2]

    The drawing has been dated 1898 but Delacroix's painting
was in a private collection until 1902 when it was given to the
Louvre.[3] Signac made a drawing with reed pen and India ink
c. 1902/03, after Delacroix's *Heliodorus driven from the Temple*
(Church of Saint Sulpice) that is very similar in character to
Matisse's copy. Signac certainly influenced Matisse's perception
of Delacroix. His essay, 'De Delacroix au Néo-Impressionisme',
which was published serially in 1898 in *La Revue Blanche*,
portrayed Delacroix as the first self-conscious colourist. While
Matisse and Signac referred to the colour theories of Delacroix
and others when painting at Collioure, their early monochromatic drawn copies show us they also looked to Delacroix's work
for studies of value not hue.[4]

    Throughout his life, Matisse was a prolific draughtsman but
his early drawings remain, for the most part, insufficiently
studied. Although Matisse painted numerous copies during his
years in the studios of Moreau, Cormon, and Carrière, he seems
to have made few drawings from works of art from the past such
as this one. Indeed, he copied little later in life, the sole exceptions
being the preparatory studies he made for his painting of 1915,
Variation on a Still Life by de Heem (Museum of Modern Art, New
York).[5]
    C.L.

Fig 67-1 Eugène Delacroix *Abduction of Rebecca*. Musée du Louvre, Paris

1   See Schneider 1984, 61. Furthermore, Matisse may have seen drawings
by van Gogh and the retrospective exhibition of 1901 held at Bernheim-
Jeune, see Gordon 1974, I, 53.
2   See, for example, *La Japonaise: Woman beside the Water* reproduced in
Elderfield 1976, 42, where the author also discusses the origins and development of Fauvism.
3   On the date, see Bock 1981. See Johnson 1986, III, no. 326, for the
provenance of the painting by Delacroix. The period from 1901 to 1904,
Matisse's 'dark years', was a time when Matisse abandoned his pointillist
technique to explore problems of drawing and volume in nuanced, subtly
hued works, thus it is likely that this drawing dates between 1902 and 1904.

4   The copy by Signac is dated by Mme. Ginette Signac and reproduced
in Paris 1963 (III), no. 104. On the influence of Signac and other neo-
impressionists on Matisse, see Bock 1981. Cézanne copied an earlier version
of Delacroix's *Abduction of Rebecca* (Metropolitan Museum of Art), probably
from a reproduction. For a reproduction of the drawing (location unknown),
see Chappuis 1973, no. 117.
5   Most of the early drawings are in the Musée Matisse at Le Cateau,
see Carlson, in Baltimore 1971, 13. These drawings are the subject of a disser-
tation, Cowart 1972. Matisse's copy after de Heem is discussed and reproduced in Elderfield 1978, 105–107, 207–208, figs. 88 and 89.

68 Smoker leaning on a Table

Juan Gris

Madrid 1887–Paris 1927

68 Smoker leaning on a Table
After Cézanne

Pencil
220 × 170 mm
Provenance: Galerie Louise Leiris

Fig 68-1 Paul Cézanne *Smoker*. Stadtliche Kunsthalle, Mannheim

Bibliography: Gaya Nuño 0 1974, 81, fig. 98
Exhibitions: Paris 1965, no. 29; Baden-Baden 1974, no. Z23;
    Bielefeld 1979, no. 213.

Mannheim, Stadtische Kunsthalle

The integration of the figure within its setting is the aspect of
Cézanne's painting (Fig. 68–1) which Gris further articulates
in his copy. He achieves this integration by extending the lines
that define the forms beyond and into the surrounding space.
None of Gris's studies after Cézanne of 1916, however, reduce
their example to such an extreme degree of linear scaffolding.
Others after figural compositions, Cézanne's *Self-Portrait*, his *Portrait of Mme. Cézanne*, or the *Bathers* then in Matisse's collection,
for example, emphasize Cézanne's divisions of light and shade
rather than the fusion of figure and ground. The lack of

Fig 68-2 Pablo Picasso *Smoker sitting at a Table*. Musée Picasso, Paris

chiaroscuro modelling in this drawing gives it a reductive quality which heralds Gris's synthetic cubist works after 1917.

This drawing is part of a larger scheme in which Gris returned to the figure after three years of painting still-lifes. It is based on the study not of life but of art.[1] In addition to Cézanne, Gris turned to Corot and even Velazquez as models for studies which culminated in his canvas of 1916, the *Portrait of Mme. Gris*.[2] After this and a similar foray into landscape, Gris returned almost exclusively to still-life for the remainder of his career.

Cézanne's catalytic role in the development of Analytic Cubism has long been recognized. The Cubists adapted not only his style but also his subject matter, turning into canonical images his *Bathers*, *Smokers*, and *Cardplayers*, as well as his still-lifes. Picasso's seated figure studies from the summer of 1914 (Fig. 68-2), clearly derive from Cézanne's *Cardplayers* and like Gris's copy remake into synthetic cubist images the work of the grandfather of Cubism.

C.L.

1   Green 1982, 92–93.
2   Reproduced in Cooper 1977, no. 202.

Jacques Villon

Normandy 1875–Puteaux 1963

69 Study of the 'Olympia'
After Manet

Black chalk
405 × 583 mm
Inscribed lower left: *Etude au crayon pour le Manet*; signed lower
centre: *Jacques Villon*
Provenance: Hannover Gallery, London; R.M. Light
Bibliography: Maison 1966, 145, pl. 186

New York, Walter Klein

In this drawing after Manet's *Olympia* now in the Musée d'Orsay
(Fig. 69–1), Villon constructed a cubist web of crystalline facets
which simultaneously dissects and defines the human form. Villon's 'décomposition constructive' is not so much an analysis of
Manet's linear structure and modelling as it is the overlay of
a decorative play of lines. Ultimately, this linear framework has
its origins in the theories of Bergson which were discussed in Villon's studio amongst members of the Puteaux group.[1] But the
lack of any particular theoretical underpinning in Villon's postwar work accounts, to some extent, for the patterned, decorative
quality of this drawing.

The drawing is a preparatory study for one of a series of colour acquatints that Villon made during the 1920s on commission
from Bernheim-Jeune.[2] The prints are all 'interprétations', as
Villon himself called them, after famous works by his French
contemporaries and predecessors. The introduction to the catalogue of the exhibition of acquatints held at Bernheim-Jeune in
1928 describes Villon's procedure stressing the lack of mechanical means. The artist would square off the canvas with threads
afixed to the frame and transcribe from a mirror the image in
reverse with metalpoint onto the copper plate. Nowhere is the
role of preparatory drawings discussed; indeed, the present
drawing is the only known preparatory study relating to the
series.

As the canonical modern image of the female nude, Manet's
Olympia has been subject to satire. Cézanne painted *A Modern
Olympia* in 1870 and included the client-viewer present only
implicitly in Manet's painting. Picasso drew a *Parody of Olympia*
in 1901 (Private collection) in which he depicted himself nude
sitting beside a black Olympia.[3]

C.L.

1   On the reaction to the cubist inventions of Braque and Picasso and the
theoretical discussions that took place amongst members of the Puteaux
group, all of whom exhibited at the 'Section d'Or' in 1912, see Rosenblum
1976, 157–200 and Buffalo 1967.

2   Reproduced in Ginestet and Pouillon 1979, no. E647.

3   Discussed and reproduced in Paris-New York 1983, no. 63. For contemporary adaptations of the *Olympia*, see Paris 1983.

69 Study of the 'Olympia'

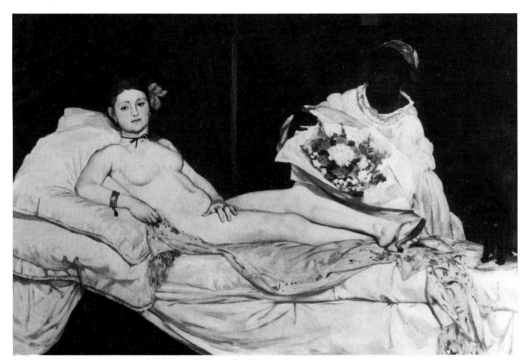

Fig 69-1 Edouard Manet *Olympia*. Musée d'Orsay, Paris

70 Le Moulin de la Galette

Raoul Dufy

Le Havre 1877–Nice 1954

70 Le Moulin de la Galette
After Renoir

Gouache
  490 × 635 mm
Inscribed and signed lower left: *d'après Renoir/Raoul Dufy*
Provenance: B. Reysz

Fig 70-1 Pierre-August Renoir *Moulin de la Galette*. Musée d'Orsay, Paris

Bibliography: Guillon-Laffaille 1982, II, no. 1985 (with further
  references)
Exhibitions: Paris 1972, no. 24; Paris 1976, no. 76; Liège 1980,
  no. 65; Copenhagen 1980, no. 70

Paris, Musée d'Art Moderne de la Ville de Paris. Inv. no. AMD
  791

It is apt that Dufy should have copied Renoir: both artists are
often spoken of in reference to masters of the French rococo,
Boucher and Watteau; both have been criticized for the decorative quality of their work. Renoir's *Moulin de la Galette* (Fig.
70–1) interested Dufy for its play of coloured light and dappled
shade on the Parisian figures. He recreated this in his own style
emphasizing the rhythmic movement and decorative patterns
with short, curving lines.

   This copy belongs to a stage late in Dufy's career when he
returned to the study of old masters. Four other drawings and

six paintings after the *Moulin de la Galette*, some inscribed 'Renoir interprété par Raoul Dufy' are among the numerous series of copies, both painted and drawn, after works such as Titian's *Lute Player*, Botticelli's *Birth of Venus*, Tintoretto's *Susanna at the Bath*, and others by Constantin Guys, El Greco, and Claude Lorrain.[1]

The works of Renoir have rarely served copyists. An interpretation by Picasso of Renoir's *Portrait of Sisley and his Wife* (Cat. no. 71) remains one of the best known drawings after Renoir.[2] In keeping with their fundamentally different artistic principles, Picasso and Dufy realized copies that are diametrically opposed. Yet, in emphatically imposing their own styles on the chosen models, they shared a similar attitude towards the act of copying.

C.L.

1   See Guillon-Laffaille 1982, II, nos. 1977–1996 and Laffaille 1977, IV, nos. 1606–1631.
2   Musée Picasso, MP 868, reproduced in London-Paris-Boston 1985, no. 9, fig. a.

Pablo Picasso

Malaga 1881–Mougins 1973

71 The Sisley Family
After Renoir

Pencil
   312 × 238 mm
Inscribed upper right: *Le menage/Sisley*
Provenance: Donation Picasso
Bibliography: Zervos 1932, III, no. 428; Lucas 1955, 37; Zervos
   1960, 14, repr.; Pool 1967, 204; Blunt 1968, 191; London-
   Paris-Boston 1985, no. 9, fig. a
Exhibitions: New York 1980, 199, repr.; Minneapolis 1980,
   no. 51

Paris, Musée Picasso. Inv. no. MP 868

Throughout his life Picasso derived an impetus for his own creations from the works of art from the past. The relationship is often documented in Picasso's drawings that reflect on the art of his predecessors. He would veil his sources to a greater or lesser extent but ultimately made them his own by imposing his personal concepts on the model. In this drawing of 1919, he reinterpreted Renoir's *Portrait of Sisley and his Wife* (Fig. 71–1) in his neo-classical manner. Picasso reduced his model to a simple line drawing, abstract in its lack of modelling yet faithful at the same time. Details such as Madame Sisley's eyes recall in their slight displacement those of his figures from 1906 influenced by Iberian sculpture while her somewhat bloated hands announce his 'colossal' style of the 1920s.

Picasso employed this linear approach for portraits in the years between 1918 and 1923, participating in the broader postwar phenomenon of a return to figuration. Picasso may have been drawn to this double portrait for its subject matter which fits into his lifelong obsession with the theme of the relationship between man and woman already clearly apparent in *La Vie* of 1903 (Cleveland Museum of Art) and finally expressed, with a different dimension, in his depictions of the painter and his model.

Picasso interpreted Renoir's painting twice more, also in drawings, each with greater degrees of modelling.[1] To copy a work and then subject it to further interpretations became Picasso's practice, particularly after 1954 when he embarked on his long series of paintings and drawings after Delacroix, Velázquez, Manet, and Poussin.[2] For Picasso, copying was a means of discovery which also permitted him to confront the old masters, to compare himself to them, to critique them, and to learn from them.

   C.L.

1   Reproduced in Lucas 1955, 14.
2   On the respective series, see Steinberg 1972, Sabartes 1959, Cooper 1962, and Schiff 1986.

71 The Sisley Family

Fig 71-1 Pierre-Auguste Renoir *Portrait of Sisley and his Wife*. Wallraf-
Richartz Museum, Cologne

Bibliography

D'Agen 1926

B. d'Agen, *Ingres. Dessinateur des Antiques*, Paris 1926.

Alazard 1950

J. Alazard, *Ingres et l'Ingrisme*, Paris 1950.

Ananoff 1961–70

A. Ananoff, *L'Oeuvre dessiné de Jean Honoré Fragonard, 1732–1806*, 4 vols., Paris 1961–70.

Ananoff 1976

A. Ananoff, *François Boucher. Peintures*, 2 vols., Paris 1976.

Ananoff and Wildenstein 1976

A. Ananoff and M.D. Wildenstein, *François Boucher*, 2 vols., Lausanne and Paris 1976.

Andrews 1964

K. Andrews, *The Nazarenes. A Brotherhood of German Painters in Rome*, Oxford 1964.

Andrews 1985

K. Andrews, *Catalogue of Netherlandish Drawings in the National Gallery of Scotland*, 2 vols., Edinburgh 1985.

Anzelewsky 1971

F. Anzelewsky, *Albrecht Dürer. Das Malerische Werk*, Berlin 1971.

Anzelewsky and Mielke 1984

F. Anzelewsky and H. Mielke, *Albrecht Dürer. Kritischer Katalog der Zeichnungen*, Staatliche Museen Preussischer Kulturbesitz, Berlin 1984 (with *Bildbund*, 1972).

Art News 1963

'Coming auctions', *Art News*, LXI, Jan. 1963, 9.

Bacou 1967

R. Bacou, 'Mariette, La collection de dessins', in Paris 1967, 17–23.

Balis 1986

A. Balis, *Corpus Rubenianum Ludwig Burchard. XVIII. Landscape and Hunting Scenes II*, Oxford 1986.

Ballarin 1967

A. Ballarin, 'Jacopo Bassano e lo studio di Raffaello e dei Salviati', *Arte Veneta*, XXI, 1967, 77–101.

De Barcia 1906

A.M. de Barcia, *Catálogo de la Colección de Dibujos Originales de Biblioteca Nacional*, Madrid 1906.

Barr 1954

A.H. Barr, ed., *Masters of Modern Art. The Museum of Modern Art*, New York 1954.

Bartsch 1803–21

A. Bartsch, *Le Peintre-graveur*, 21 vols., Vienna 1803–21.

Bean et al. 1982

J. Bean with the assistance of L. Turčić, *15th and 16th Century Italian Drawings in the Metropolitan Museum of Art*, New York 1982.

Beau 1968

M. Beau, *La Collection des dessins d'Hubert Robert au Musée de Valence*, Lyon 1968.

Beckett 1962–68

R.B. Beckett, ed., *John Constable's Correspondence*, 6 vols., Suffolk Records Society, 1962–68.

Belkin 1984

K. Belkin, 'Rubens und Stimmer', in Basel 1984, 200–206.

Benesch 1935

O. Benesch, *Rembrandt. Werk und Forschung*, Vienna 1935.

Benesch 1954–57

O. Benesch, *The Drawings of Rembrandt. A Critical and Chronological Catalogue*, 6 vols., London 1954–57.

Berenson 1938

B. Berenson, *The Drawings of the Florentine Painters*, Chicago 1938.

Bernt 1980

W. Bernt, *Die niederländischen Maler und Zeichner des 17. Jahrhunderts*, 5 vols., 2nd ed., Munich 1980.

Berthold 1958

G. Berthold, *Cézanne und die alten Meister*, Stuttgart 1958.

Bethe 1930/31

H. Bethe, 'Eine Pseudoantike des Cinquecento und ihr Echo in der Kunst des XVII. und XVIII. Jahrhunderts', *Zeitschrift für bildende Kunst*, LXIV, 1930/31, 181–184.

Bierens de Haan 1948

J.C.J. Bierens de Haan, *L'Oeuvre gravé de Cornelius Cort, graveur hollandais, 1533–1578*, The Hague 1948.

Bindman 1978

D. Bindman, *The Complete Graphic Works of William Blake*, London 1978.

Bloch 1946

E.M. Bloch, 'Rembrandt and the Lopez Collection', *Gazette des Beaux-Arts*, XXIX, 1946, 175–186.

Blunt 1958

A. Blunt, *Nicolas Poussin*, Washington 1958.

Blunt 1966

A. Blunt, *The Paintings of Nicolas Poussin. A Critical Catalogue*, London 1966.

Blunt 1968

A. Blunt, 'Picasso's Classical Period (1917–25)', *Burlington Magazine*, CX, 1968, 187–191.

Blunt 1974

A. Blunt, 'Newly Identified Drawings by Poussin and his Followers', *Master Drawings*, XII, 1974, 239–248.

Blunt 1979

A. Blunt, *The Drawings of Poussin*, New Haven and London 1979.

Bock 1981

C. Bock, *Henri Matisse and Neo-Impressionism 1898–1908*, Ann Arbor 1981.

Bock 1921

E. Bock, *Zeichnungen deutscher Meister im Kupferstichkabinett zu Berlin*, 2 vols., Berlin 1921.

Bock and Rosenberg 1930, 1931

E. Bock and J. Rosenberg, *Staatliche Museen zu Berlin. Die niederländischen Meister*, Berlin 1930, Frankfurt-am-Main 1931.

Bode 1908
W.v. Bode, 'Pieter Lastmans Gemälde der Susanna mit den Alten und seine Beziehungen zu den Darstellungen des Gleichen Motivs von Rembrandt', *Amtliche Berichte aus den königlichen Kunstsammlungen*, XXX, 1908, 58–66.

Boggs 1958
J.S. Boggs, 'Degas Notebooks at the Bibliothèque Nationale', *Burlington Magazine*, C, 1958, 163–171, 196–205, 240–246.

Boime 1971
A. Boime, *The Academy and French Painting in the Nineteenth Century*, London 1971.

Bolten 1967
J. Bolten, *Dutch Drawings from the Collection of Dr. C. Hofstede de Groot*, Utrecht 1967.

Bolten 1970
J. Bolten, 'Een Landschaptekening van Herman Saftleven', *Opstellen voor H. van de Waal*, Amsterdam 1970, 9–17.

Bolten 1985
J. Bolten, *Method and Practice. Dutch and Flemish Drawing Books 1600–1750*, London 1985.

Boon 1978
K.G. Boon, *Catalogue of the Dutch and Flemish Drawings in the Rijksmuseum. Netherlandish Drawings of the Fifteenth and Sixteenth Centuries*, 2 vols., The Hague 1978.

Boucher and Jaccottet 1952
F. Boucher and P. Jaccottet, *Le Dessin français au XVIIIe siècle*, Lausanne 1952.

Bredius 1936, 1937
A. Bredius, ed., *The Paintings of Rembrandt*, Vienna 1936, London 1937.

Brejon de Lavergnée et al. 1979
A. Brejon de Lavergnée, J. Foucart, and N. Reynaud, *Catalogue sommaire illustré des peintures du Musée du Louvre. I. Ecoles flamande et hollandaise*, Paris 1979.

Broos 1980
B. Broos, 'Rembrandts Indische Miniaturen', *Spiegel Historiael*, IV, 1980, 210–218.

Budde 1930
I. Budde, *Beschreibender Katalog der Handzeichnungen in der Staatlichen Kunstakademie Düsseldorf*, Düsseldorf 1930.

Burchard and d'Hulst 1963
L. Burchard and R.-A. d'Hulst, *Rubens Drawings*, 2 vols., Brussels 1963.

Busch 1973
G. Busch, *Eugène Delacroix. Der Tod des Valentin*, Frankfurt-am-Main 1973.

Butlin 1962
M. Butlin, *Turner Watercolours*, London 1962.

Byam Shaw 1976
J. Byam Shaw, *Drawings by Old Masters at Christ Church, Oxford*, 2 vols., Oxford 1976.

Byam Shaw 1983
J. Byam Shaw, *The Italian Drawings of the Frits Lugt Collection*, 3 vols., Paris 1983.

Cailleux 1959
J. Cailleux, 'Robert à pris modèle sur Boucher', *Connaissance des Arts*, 1959, 100–107.

Cellini/Symonds 1903
B. Cellini, *The Life of Benvenuto Cellini*, ed. and trans. by J.A. Symonds, New York 1903.

Chappuis 1973
A. Chappuis, *The Drawings of Paul Cézanne. A Catalogue Raisonné*, 2 vols., Greenwich 1973.

Clark 1952
K. Clark, *Leonardo da Vinci*, Cambridge 1952.

Clark 1966
K. Clark, *Rembrandt and the Italian Renaissance*, London 1966.

Clark and Pedretti 1968
K. Clark and C. Pedretti, *Leonardo da Vinci Drawings at Windsor Castle*, 2nd ed., London 1968.

Clément 1879
C. Clément, *Géricault*, Paris 1879.

***Cleveland* 1979**
'The Year in Review for 1978', *Cleveland Museum Bulletin*, LXVI, 1979, 3.

***Cleveland* 1981**
'The Year in Review for 1980', *Cleveland Museum Bulletin*, LXVIII, 1981, 190.

Coffin 1951
D. Coffin, 'Tintoretto and the Medici Tombs', *Art Bulletin*, XXXIII, 1951, 119–125.

Cooper 1962
D. Cooper, *Pablo Picasso. Les Déjeuners*, Paris 1962.

Cooper 1977
D. Cooper, *Juan Gris. Catalogue raisonné*, 2 vols., Paris 1977.

Cormack 1986
M. Cormack, *Constable*, Cambridge 1986.

Cowart 1972
J. Cowart, '*Ecoliers*' to '*Fauves*'; *Matisse, Marquet, and Manguin Drawings: 1890–1906*, diss., Johns Hopkins University, Baltimore 1972.

Crowe and Cavalcaselle 1871
J.A. Crowe and G.B. Cavalcaselle, *A History of Painting in North Italy*, London 1871.

Crowe and Cavalcaselle 1923
J.A. Crowe and G.B. Cavalcaselle, *A History of Painting in North Italy*, 3rd ed., ed. with an introduction by L. Douglas, London 1923.

Davies 1928
R. Davies, 'Thomas Girtin in Paris', *Burlington Magazine*, LII, 1928, 221–222.

Degenhart and Schmitt 1968
B. Degenhart and A. Schmitt, *Corpus der italienischen Zeichnungen 1300–1450*, Berlin 1968.

Denucé 1932
J. Denucé, *De Antwerpsche 'Konstkamers'*, Antwerp 1932.

***Dizionario* 1979**
'G.B. Cavalcaselle', unsigned entry in *Dizionario Biografico degli Italiani*, XXII, Rome 1979, 640–644.

Dussler 1959
L. Dussler, *Die Zeichnungen des Michelangelo*, Berlin 1959.

Eaves 1982
M. Eaves, *William Blake's Theory of Art*, Princeton 1982.

Eisler 1958
C. Eisler, 'The Egmont Albums. A New Collection of Drawings for Yale', *Yale University Library Gazette*, XXXII, no. 3, 1958, 86–87.

Eitner 1971
L. Eitner, 'Dessins de Géricault d'après Rubens: La Genèse du "Radeau de la Meduse"', *Revue de l'Art*, XIV, 1971, 51–56.

Eitner 1972
L. Eitner, *Géricault's Raft of the Medusa*, London 1972.

Elderfield 1976
J. Elderfield, *The 'Wild Beasts', Fauvism and Its Affinities*, Museum of Modern Art, New York 1976.

Elderfield 1978
J. Elderfield, *Matisse in the Collection of the Museum of Modern Art*, New York 1978.

Erdman 1969
D.R. Erdman, *Blake, Prophet Against Empire*, Princeton 1969.

Escholier 1926–29
R. Escholier, *Delacroix, Peintre, Graveur, Ecrivain*, 3 vols., Paris 1926–29.

Ettinghausen 1961
R. Ettinghausen, *Paintings of the Sultans and Emperors of India in American Collections*, New Delhi 1961.

Facsimiles 1825
Facsimiles extraits des livres de croquis de Géricault et Lithographies par plusieurs artistes, Paris 1825.

Fairfax Murray 1905–12
C. Fairfax Murray, *J. Pierpont Morgan Collection of Drawings by the Old Masters formed by C. Fairfax Murray*, London 1905–12.

Federmann 1927
A. Federmann, *Johann Heinrich Füssli. Dichter und Maler 1741–1825*, Zürich and Leipzig 1927.

Forster-Hahn 1967
F. Forster-Hahn, 'The Sources of True Taste: Benjamin West's Instructions to a Young Painter for his Studies in Italy', *Journal of the Warburg and Courtauld Institutes*, XXX, 1967, 367–382.

Freise 1911
K. Freise, *Pieter Lastman*, Berlin 1911.

Frey 1909–11
K. Frey, *Die Handzeichnungen Michelagniolos Buonarroti*, 3 vols., Berlin 1909–11.

Friedländer and Blunt 1939–74
W. Friedländer and A. Blunt, *The Drawings of Nicolas Poussin*, 5 vols., London 1939–74.

Fries 1964
G. Fries, 'Degas et les maîtres', *Art de France*, IV, 1964, 352–359.

Fubini and Held 1964
G. Fubini and J. Held, 'Padre Resta's Rubens Drawings after Ancient Sculpture', *Master Drawings*, II, 1964, 123–141.

Fuchs 1969
R.H. Fuchs, *Rembrandt in Amsterdam*, Greenwich 1969.

Galichon 1861
E. Galichon, 'Description des Dessins de M. Ingres exposés au Salon des Arts-Unis', *Gazette des Beaux-Arts*, 1861, 343–362.

Ganeval 1976
C. Ganeval, 'Delacroix et les maîtres allemands du XVIe siècle', *Pantheon*, XXXIV, 1976, 40–48.

Gantner 1962
J. Gantner, 'Rembrandt und das Abendmahl des Leonardo', *Variae formae veritas una, Kunsthistorische Studien, Festschrift Friedrich Gerke*, Baden-Baden 1962, 179–184.

Gantner 1964
J. Gantner, *Rembrandt und die Verwandlung klassischer Formen*, Bern and Munich 1964.

Ganz 1961
P. Ganz, *The Paintings of Hans Holbein. First Complete Edition*, London 1961.

Gassier and Wilson 1971
P. Gassier and J. Wilson, *The Life and Complete Works of Francisco Goya*, New York 1971.

Gassier 1975
P. Gassier, *The Drawings of Goya. The Sketches, Studies and Individual Drawings*, New York 1975.

Gaya Nuño 1974
J.A. Gaya Nuño, *Juan Gris*, Paris 1974.

Van Gelder 1957
J.G. van Gelder, 'Verloren Werken van Lucas van Leyden', *Miscellanea Prof. Dr. D. Roggen*, Antwerp 1957, 91–100.

Van Gelder 1971
J.G. van Gelder, 'Jan de Bisschop', *Oud Holland*, LXXXVI, 1971, no. 4, 1–59.

Van Gelder and Jost 1985
J.G. van Gelder and I. Jost *Jan de Bisschop and his ICONES & PARADIGMATA*, ed. by K. Andrews, Amsterdam 1985.

Gerson 1968
H. Gerson, *Rembrandt Paintings*, New York 1968.

Gilbert 1961
C. Gilbert, 'Tintoretto and Michelangelo's St. Damian', *Burlington Magazine*, CIII, 1961, 16–20.

Gilbert 1969
C. Gilbert, 'The Drawings now associated with Masaccio's Sagra', *Storia dell'arte*, no. 3, 1969, 260–277.

Ginestet and Pouillon 1979
C. Ginestet and C. Pouillon, *Jacques Villon. Les Estampes et les illustrations. Catalogue Raisonné*, Paris 1979.

Girtin and Loshak 1954
T. Girtin and D. Loshak, *The Art of Thomas Girtin*, London 1954.

Glendinning 1977
N. Glendinning, *Goya and his Critics*, New Haven and New York 1977.

Glück and Haberditzl 1928
G. Glück and F.M. Haberditzl, *Die Handzeichnungen von Peter Paul Rubens*, Berlin 1928.

Glück 1933
H. Glück, *Asiatische Miniaturenmalerei*, Klagenfurt 1933.

Goldscheider 1959
L. Goldscheider, *Leonardo da Vinci*, London 1959.

Goncourt 1882
E. and J. de Goncourt: *L'Art du dix-huitième siècle*, 3rd ed., Paris 1882.

Gordon 1974
D. Gordon, *Modern Art Exhibitions. 1900–1916*, 2 vols., Munich 1974.

Gould 1975
C. Gould, *National Gallery Catalogues. The Sixteenth Century Italian Schools*, London 1975.

Gradmann 1949
E. Gradmann, *Französische Meisterzeichnungen des 18. Jahrhunderts*, New York 1949.

Green 1982
C. Green, 'Synthesis and the "Synthetic Process" in the Painting of Juan Gris 1915–19', *Art History*, V, 1982, 87–105.

Guillon-Laffaille 1982
F. Guillon-Laffaille, *Raoul Dufy. Catalogue raisonné des aquarelles, gouaches et pastels*, 2 vols., Paris 1982.

Guiraud 1913
L. Guiraud, *Dessins de l'école française du XVIIIe siècle provenant de la collection H.*, Paris 1913.

Haak 1969
B. Haak, *Rembrandt*, New York 1969.

Hartt 1958
F. Hartt, *Giulio Romano*, 2 vols., New Haven 1958.

Hartt 1970
F. Hartt, *Michelangelo's Drawings*, New York 1970.

Hartt 1981
F. Hartt, *Giulio Romano*, 2 vols., New York 1981.

Haskell and Penny 1981
F. Haskell and N. Penny, *Taste and the Antique. The Lure of Classical Sculpture 1500–1900*, New Haven and London 1981.

Hattis 1973
P. Harris, *Ingres' Sculptural Style*, Cambridge, MA 1973.

Haverkamp-Begemann 1957
E. Haverkamp-Begemann, *Vijf eeuwen Tekenkunst. Tekeningen van Europese Meester in het Boymans Museum te Rotterdam*, Rotterdam 1957.

Haverkamp-Begemann et al. 1964
E. Haverkamp-Begemann, S.D. Lawder, and C.W. Talbot, Jr., *Drawings from the Clark Art Institute. A Catalogue raisonné of the Robert Sterling Clark Collection of European and American Drawings. 16th through 19th Centuries*, New Haven 1964.

Haverkamp-Begemann and Logan 1970
E. Haverkamp-Begemann and A.-M. Logan *European Drawings and Watercolors in the Yale University Art Gallery. 1500–1900*, 2 vols., New Haven and London 1970.

Held 1931
J.S. Held, *Dürer's Wirkung auf die niederländische Kunst seiner Zeit*, The Hague 1931.

Held 1959
J.S. Held, *Rubens. Selected Drawings*, 2 vols., London 1959.

Held 1982
J.S. Held, 'Rubens and Titian', in *Titian, his World and his Legacy*, ed. by D. Rosand, New York 1982, 306.

Held 1986
J.S. Held, *Rubens. Selected Drawings*, 2nd ed., New Haven and Oxford 1986.

Hell 1930
H. Hell, 'Die späten Handzeichnungen Rembrandts', *Repertorium für Kunstwissenschaft*, LI, 1930, 92–140.

Henkel 1930
M.D. Henkel, 'Theodoor Matham', *Thieme-Becker*, XXIV, 1930.

Herbert 1962
R.L. Herbert, *Seurat's Drawings*, New York 1962.

Heydenreich 1974
L.H. Heydenreich, *Leonardo. The Last Supper*, New York 1974.

Hind 1923
A.M. Hind, *Catalogue of Dutch and Flemish Drawings in the British Museum. II. Drawings by Rubens, van Dyck, and Other Artists of the Flemish School of the XVIIth Century*, London 1923.

Hind 1932
A.M. Hind, *Rembrandt*, Cambridge 1932.

Hind 1938–48
A.M. Hind, *Early Italian Engraving. A critical catalogue with complete reproduction of all the prints described*, 7 vols., London 1938–48.

Hirschmann 1919
O. Hirschmann, *Hendrick Goltzius*, Leipzig 1919.

Hirschmann 1921
O. Hirschmann, *Verzeichnes des graphischen Werks von Hendrick Goltzius. 1558–1617*, Leipzig 1921.

Hoetink 1968
H.R. Hoetink, *Franse Tekeningen uit de 19e eeuw. Catalogus van de verzameling in het Museum Boymans-van Beuningen*, Rotterdam 1968.

Hoff 1938
U. Hoff, 'Rubens Drawings, Some Notes', *Old Master Drawings*, XIII, 1938, 10–18.

Hofstede de Groot 1894
C. Hofstede de Groot, 'Entlehnungen Rembrandts', *Jahrbuch der königlich preussischen Kunstsammlungen*, XV, 1894, 175–181.

Hofstede de Groot 1906
C. Hofstede de Groot, *Die Handzeichnungen Rembrandts*, Haarlem 1906.

Hollstein 1949–
F.W.H. Hollstein, *Dutch and Flemish Etchings, Engravings and Woodcuts. ca. 1450–1700*, 30 vols., Amsterdam 1949–.

Hoogewerff 1931
G.J. Hoogewerff, 'Waneer en hoe vaak was Berchem in Italie?', *Oud Holland*, XLVIII, 1931, 84–87.

Houbraken 1718–21
A. Houbraken, *De Groote Schouburgh der Nederlantsche Konstschilders en Schilderessen*, Amsterdam 1718–21.

Howard 1969
D. Howard, 'Some Eighteenth-Century English Followers of Claude', *Burlington Magazine*, CXI, 1969, 726–732.

Hyatt Major 1978/79
A. Hyatt Major, 'Rembrandt and the Bible', *Metropolitan Museum of Art Bulletin*, N.S. XXXVI, Winter 1978/79, 2–48.

Inventaire De Grez 1913
Inventaire des Dessins et Aquarelles donnés à l'Etat Belge par Madame la Douairière de Grez, Brussels 1913.

Irwin 1966
D. Irwin, *English Neoclassical Art: Studies in Inspiration and Taste*, London 1966.

Jacobus 1972
J. Jacobus, *Matisse*, New York 1972.

Jacoby 1979
B.S. Jacoby, 'A Landscape Drawing by François Boucher after Domenico Campagnola', *Master Drawings*, XVII, 1979, 261–272.

Jacoby 1986

B.S. Jacoby, *François Boucher's Early Development as a Draughtsman. 1720–1734*, New York and London 1986.

Jaffé 1954

M. Jaffé, 'Rubens and the Influence of Italy', *The Listener*, LI, 1954, 135–137.

Jaffé 1956

M. Jaffé, 'Rubens Drawings at Antwerp', *Burlington Magazine*, XCVIII, 1956, 314–321.

Jaffé 1965

M. Jaffé, 'Rubens as a Draughtsman', *Burlington Magazine*, CVII, 1965, 372–381.

Jaffé 1966

M. Jaffé, 'Rubens as a Collector of Drawings, Part Three', *Master Drawings*, IV, 1966, 127–148.

Jaffé 1967

M. Jaffé, 'Rubens and Raphael', *Studies in Renaissance and Baroque Art Presented to Anthony Blunt*, London 1967, 98–107

Jaffé 1977

M. Jaffé, *Rubens and Italy*, Oxford 1977.

Jamot 1932

P. Jamot, 'Goethe et Delacroix', *Gazette des Beaux-Arts*, 6e ser., VIII, 1932, 279–298.

Jenni 1976

U. Jenni, *Das Skizzenbuch der Internationalen Gotik in der Uffizien: der Übergang vom Musterbuch zum Skizzenbuch*, Vienna 1976.

Johnson 1981–86

L. Johnson, *The Paintings of Eugène Delacroix. A Critical Catalogue*, 4 vols., Oxford 1981–86.

Joubin 1932

A. Joubin, ed., *Journal de Eugène Delacroix*, 3 vols., Paris 1932.

Jungmaker 1938

G. Jungmaker, 'Sergels Faun: till fragan am dess forebilder', *Nationalmusei Arsbock*, Stockholm, N.S. VIII, 1938, 132–136.

Kamenskaya 1937

T. Kamenskaya, 'Unveröffentlichte Zeichnungen Abraham Bloemaerts in der Hermitage', *Oud-Holland*, LIV, 1937, 145–163.

Kauffmann 1924 (I)

H. Kauffmann, *Albrecht Dürers rhythmische Kunst*, Leipzig 1924.

Kauffmann 1924 (II)

H. Kauffmann, 'Rembrandts Berliner Susanna', *Jahrbuch der preussischen Kunstsammlungen*, XLV, 1924, 72–80.

Keay 1974

C. Keay, *Henry Fuseli*, London and New York 1974.

Kitson 1978

M. Kitson, *Claude Lorrain. 'Liber Veritatis'*, London 1978.

Klemm 1986

C. Klemm, *Joachim von Sandrart*, Berlin 1986.

Kliman 1982

E.T. Kliman, 'Delacroix's Lions and Tigers: A Link between Man and Nature', *Art Bulletin*, LXIV, 1982, 446–466.

Knab et al. 1983

E. Knab, E. Mitsch, K. Oberhuber, *Raphael. Die Zeichnungen*, Vienna 1983.

Knowles 1831

J. Knowles, *The Life and Writings of Henry Fuseli*, II, London 1831.

Knowlton 1942

J. Knowlton, 'Stylistic Origins of Géricault's *Raft of the Medusa*', Marsyas II, 1942, 125–144.

Koegler 1926

H. Koegler, *Die Basler Handzeichnungen des Nikolaus Manuel Deutsch*, Basel 1926.

Koevoets et al. 1976

B. Koevoets, E. van Uitert and E.K.J. Reznicek, *Oude tekeningen in het bezit van de Gemeentmusea van Amsterdam waaronder de collectie Fordor*, I, *Italie 15e–18e eeuw*, Amsterdam 1976.

Koschatzky 1970

W. Koschatzky, *Watercolour. History and Technique*, London 1970.

Koschatzky and Strobl 1972

W. Koschatzky and A. Strobl, *Dürer Drawings in the Albertina*, Greenwich 1972.

Krautheimer 1971

R. Krautheimer, *Ghiberti's Bronze Doors*. Princeton 1971.

Kutter 1907

P. Kutter, *Joachim von Sandrart als Künstler*, Strassburg 1907.

Laffaille 1977

M. Laffaille, *Raoul Dufy. Catalogue raisonné de l'oeuvre peint*, 4 vols., Geneva 1977.

Lapauze 1911

H. Lapauze, *Ingres, sa vie et son oeuvre*, Paris 1911.

Lavin 1975

M.A. Lavin, *Seventeenth-Century Barberini Documents and Inventories of Art*, New York 1975.

De Leiris 1969

A. de Leiris, *The Drawings of Edouard Manet*, Berkeley and Los Angeles 1969.

Lemoisne 1946

P.A. Lemoisne, *Degas et son oeuvre*, 4 vols., Paris 1946.

Lichtenstein 1971

S. Lichtenstein, 'Delacroix's Copies after Raphael – I and II', *Burlington Magazine*, CXIII, 1971, 525–533 and 593–603.

Lichtenstein 1977

S. Lichtenstein, 'More about Delacroix's Copies after Raphael', *Burlington Magazine*, CXIX, 1977, 503–504.

Lichtenstein 1979

S. Lichtenstein, *Delacroix and Raphael*, New York 1979.

Lippmann 1883–1929

F. Lippmann, ed. *Zeichnungen von Albrecht Dürer in Nachbildungen*, 7 vols., Berlin 1883–1929.

Lippmann 1888–1901

F. Lippmann, *Original Drawings by Rembrandt*, 2 vols., Berlin 1888–1901.

Lippmann 1905

F. Lippmann, *Zeichnungen Albrecht Dürers in der Albertina zu Wien in Nachbildungen unter Mitwirkung von Josef Edler von Schönbrunner*, Berlin 1905.

Lochhead 1982

I. Lochhead, *The Spectator and the Landscape in the Art Criticism of Diderot and His Contemporaries*, Ann Arbor 1982.

Logan 1987
A.-M. Logan, [Review of Held 1986], *Master Drawings* [in press].

Logan and Haverkamp-Begemann 1978
A.-M. Logan and E. Haverkamp-Begemann, 'Dessins de Rubens', *Revue de l'Art*, XLII, 1978, 89–99.

Lopez-Rey 1953
J. Lopez-Rey, *Goya's Caprichos. Beauty, Reason and Caricature*, 2 vols., Princeton 1953.

Lucas 1955
J. Lucas, 'Picasso as a Copyist', *Art News*, LIV, Nov. 1955, 36–39 ff.

Lüdecke and Heiland 1955
H. Lüdecke and S. Heiland, *Dürer und die Nachwelt*, Berlin 1955.

Lugt 1921, 1956
F. Lugt, *Les marques de collections de dessins et d'estampes*, Amsterdam 1921; *Supplément*, The Hague 1956.

Lugt 1931
F. Lugt, 'Beiträge zu dem Katalog der niederländischen Handzeichnungen in Berlin', *Jahrbuch der preussischen Kunstsammlungen*, LII, 1931, 36–80.

Lugt 1933
F. Lugt, *Musée du Louvre. Inventaire général des dessins des écoles du nord. Ecole hollandaise*, III, Paris 1933.

Lugt 1936 (I)
F. Lugt with J. Vallery-Radot, *Bibliothèque Nationale. Inventaire général des dessins des écoles du nord*, Paris 1936.

Lugt 1936 (II)
F. Lugt, 'Italiaansche Kunstwerken in Nederlandsche verzamelingen van vroeger tijden', *Oud Holland*, LIII, 1936, 97–135.

Lugt 1943
F. Lugt, 'Rubens and Stimmer', *Art Quarterly*, VI, 1943, 99–114.

Lugt 1952
F. Lugt, 'Rembrandt: follower and innovator', *Art News*, LI, Oct. 1952, 38–42 ff.

Lunsingh Scheurleer 1980
P. Lunsingh Scheurleer, 'Mogul-miniaturen door Rembrandt nagetekend', *De kroniek van het Rembrandthuis*, 1, 1980, XXXII, 10–40.

Magnusson 1977
B. Magnusson, 'Some Drawings by Rubens Identified in the Nationalmuseum (Stockholm)', *Nationalmuseum Bulletin* I, 1977, 70–79.

Maison 1960, 1966
K.E. Maison, *Themes and Variations. Five Centuries of Master Copies and Interpretations*, London 1960, 1966.

Mallet 1981
J.V.G. Mallet, 'Mantua and Urbino. Gonzaga Patronage of Maiolica', *Apollo*, CXIV, 1981, 162–169.

Marlier 1966
G. Marlier, *La Renaissance Flamande. Pierre Coeck d'Alost*, Brussels 1966.

Martin 1969
J. Martin, *Rubens. The Antwerp Altarpieces: The Raising of the Cross and The Descent from the Cross*, New York 1969.

Massengale 1979
J.M. Massengale, 'Drawings by Fragonard in North American Collections', *Burlington Magazine*, CXXI, 1979, 270–272.

Mathey 1945
J. Mathey, *Ingres*, Paris 1945.

Mathey 1955
J. Mathey, *Ingres, dessins*, Paris 1955.

Maurer 1985
E. Maurer, 'Stimmer in Rubens's Sicht', *Zeitschrift für schweizerische Archaeologie und Kunstgeschichte*, XLII, 1985, 83–95.

Mayne 1949
J. Mayne, *Thomas Girtin*, Leigh-on-Sea 1949.

Mende 1971
M. Mende, *Dürer – Bibliographie*, Wiesbaden 1971.

Michel 1893
E. Michel, *Rembrandt, sa vie, son oeuvre, et son temps*, Paris 1893.

Miedema 1969
H. Miedema, '"Het voorbeeldt niet te by te hebben". Over Hendrick Goltzius's tekeningen naar de antiken', *Miscellanea I.Q. van Regteren Altena*, Amsterdam 1969, 74–78.

Mireur 1911
H. Mireur, *Dictionnaire des Ventes d'Art*, IV, Paris 1911.

Mongan and Sachs 1940
A. Mongan and P.J. Sachs, *Drawings in the Fogg Museum of Art*, 3 vols., Cambridge 1940.

Mongan 1945
A. Mongan, 'Fragonard the Draughtsman', in *Fragonard: Drawings for Ariosto*, New York 1945.

Montagu 1985
J. Montagu, *Alessandro Algardi*, 2 vols. New Haven and London 1985.

Moreau-Nélaton 1873
A. Moreau-Nélaton, *Eugène Delacroix et son oeuvre*, Paris 1873.

Morris 1986
S. Morris, *Thomas Girtin, 1775–1802*, New Haven 1986.

Möseneder 1979
K. Möseneder, *Montorsoli: Die Brunnen*, Mittenwald 1979.

Muchall-Viebrook 1926
T.W. Muchall-Viebrook, *Flemish Drawings of the Seventeenth-Century*, London 1926.

Muller 1977
J.M. Muller, *Peter Paul Rubens as Collector of Art*, diss. Yale University, New Haven 1977.

Muller 1982
J.M. Muller, 'Rubens's Theory and Practice of the Imitation of Art', *Art Bulletin*, LXIV, 1982, 229–247.

Müller 1929
C. Müller, 'Studien zu Lastman und Rembrandt', *Jahrbuch der preussischen Kunstsammlungen*, XLV, 1929, 45–83.

Müller-Hofstede 1965
J. Müller-Hofstede, 'Beiträge zum Zeichnerischen Werk von Rubens', *Wallraf-Richartz-Jahrbuch*, XXVII, 1965, 261–265.

Müller-Hofstede 1966
J. Müller-Hofstede, [Review of L. Burchard and R.-A. d'Hulst 1956], *Master Drawings*, IV, 1966, 435–454.

Naef 1967/68

H. Naef, '*Ingres, dessinateur de portraits*' in Paris 1967/68, xix–xxiii.

Naef 1977–80

H. Naef, *Die Bildniszeichnungen von J.-A.-D. Ingres*, 5 vols., Bern 1977–80.

Neumann 1918

C. Neumann, *Aus der Werkstatt Rembrandts*, Heidelberg 1918.

Nolhac and Loukomski 1930

P. de Nolhac and G.-K. Loukomski, *La Rome d'Hubert Robert*, Paris 1930.

Nordenfalk 1987

C. Nordenfalk, 'L'An 1715', in *Antoine Watteau (1684–1721). The Painter, His Age and His Legend*, F. Moureau and M. Morgan Graselli, eds., Paris and Geneva 1987, 29–36.

Oldenbourg 1921

R. Oldenbourg, *Rubens des Meisters Gemälde. Klassiker der Kunst*, V, 4th ed., Stuttgart and Berlin 1921.

Pacheco 1956

F. Pacheco, *Arte de la pintura*, [1649], intro. by F.J. Sánchez-Cantón, Madrid 1956.

Panofsky 1948

E. Panofsky, *Albrecht Dürer*, 2 vols., 3rd ed., Princeton 1948.

Panofsky 1955

E. Panofsky, *The Life and Art of Albrecht Dürer*, [1943], Princeton 1955.

Parker 1931

K.T. Parker, *The Drawings of Antoine Watteau*, London 1931.

Parker 1935

K.T. Parker, 'Sidelights on Watteau', *Old Master Drawings*, X, June 1935, 3–9.

Parker 1938

K.T. Parker, *Catalogue of the Collection of Drawings in the Ashmolean Museum*, I, Oxford 1938.

Parker 1939/40

K.T. Parker, 'Some Observations on Oxford Raphaels', *Old Master Drawings*, XIV, 1939/40, 34–43.

Parker and Mathey 1957

K.T. Parker and J. Mathey, *Antoine Watteau. Catalogue complet de son oeuvre dessiné*, 2 vols., Paris 1957.

Pepper 1984

D.S. Pepper, *Guido Reni*, Oxford 1984.

Pool 1967

P. Pool, 'Picasso's Neo-Classicism: Second Period, 1917–25', *Apollo*, LXXXV, 1967, 198–207.

Popham and Wilde 1949

A.E. Popham and J. Wilde, *The Italian Drawings of the XV and XVI centuries . . . at Windsor Castle*, London 1949.

Popham 1971

A.E. Popham, *Catalogue of the Drawings of Parmigianino*, 3 vols., New Haven and London 1971.

Pope-Hennessy 1969

J. Pope-Hennessy, *Paolo Uccello*, London 1969.

Pope-Hennessy 1970

J. Pope-Hennessy, *Raphael. The Wrightsman Lectures*, New York 1970.

Pope-Hennessy 1980

J. Pope-Hennessy, *Study and Criticism of Italian Sculpture*, New York 1980.

Pope-Hennessy 1985

J. Pope-Hennessy, *Italian High Renaissance and Baroque Sculpture*. 3rd ed., New York 1985.

Portalis 1889

R. de Portalis, *Fragonard, sa vie et son oeuvre*, 2 vols., Paris 1889.

Radius and Camesasca 1968

E. Radius and E. Camesasca, *L'Opera completa di Ingres*, Milan 1968.

Rearick 1980

W.R. Rearick, *Maestri veneti del Cinquecento*, Florence 1980.

Reff 1959

T. Reff, 'Cézanne: the enigma of the nude', *Art News*, LVII, 1959, 26–29, 68.

Reff 1960

T. Reff, 'Reproductions and Books in Cézanne's Studio', *Gazette des Beaux-Arts*, 6e ser., LVI, 1960, 303–309.

Reff 1962

T. Reff, 'Cézanne's Constructive Stroke', *Art Quarterly*, XXV, 1962, 214–227.

Reff 1963

T. Reff, 'Degas's Copies of Older Art', *Burlington Magazine*, CV, 1963, 241–251.

Reff 1964 (I)

T. Reff, 'Copyists at the Louvre, 1850–1870', *Art Bulletin*, XLVI, 1964, 552–559.

Reff 1964 (II)

T. Reff, 'New Light on Degas's Copies', *Burlington Magazine*, CVI, 1964, 250–259.

Reff 1965

T. Reff, 'Addenda on Degas's Copies', *Burlington Magazine*, CVII, 1965, 320–323.

Reff 1971

T. Reff, 'Further Thoughts on Degas's Copies', *Burlington Magazine*, CXIII, 1971, 534–543.

Reff 1976 (I)

T. Reff, *Degas: The Artist's Mind*, New York 1976.

Reff 1976 (II)

T. Reff, *The Notebooks of Edgar Degas*, 2 vols., Oxford 1976.

Van Regteren Altena 1936

I.Q. van Regteren Altena, *Jacques de Gheyn, an Introduction to the Study of his Drawings*, Amsterdam 1936.

Van Regteren Altena 1948/49

I.Q. van Regteren Altena, 'Rembrandt's Way to Emmaus', *Kunstmuseets Aarsskrift*, XXXV/XXXVI, 1948/49, 1–26.

Van Regteren Altena 1962

I.Q. van Regteren Altena, *Verslagen omtrent 's Rijks Verzamelingen van Geschiedenis en Kunst 1960*, The Hague 1962, 35.

Van Regteren Altena 1967

I.Q. van Regteren Altena, 'The Origin of a Motif in Rembrandt's Work', *Master Drawings*, V, 1967, 375–378.

Van Regteren Altena 1970

I.Q. van Regteren Altena, [Review of Degenhart and Schmitt 1968], *Master Drawings*, VIII, 1970, 396–404.

Van Regteren Altena 1977

I.Q. van Regteren Altena, *Peter Paul Rubens. Drawings after Hans Holbein's Dance of Death*, Amsterdam 1977.

Van Regteren Altena 1983
I.Q. van Regteren Altena, *Jacques de Gheyn: Three Generations*, 3 vols., The Hague 1983.

Rewald 1937
J. Rewald, ed., *Paul Cézanne Correspondence*, Paris 1937.

Rewald 1983
J. Rewald, *Paul Cézanne. The Watercolours*, Boston 1983.

Reynolds 1984
G. Reynolds, *The Later Paintings and Drawings of John Constable*, 2 vols., New Haven and London 1984.

Reznicek 1960
E.K.J. Reznicek, 'Het begin van Goltzius's loopbaan als schilder', *Oud Holland*, LXXV, 1960, 30–49.

Reznicek 1961
E.K.J. Reznicek, *Die Zeichnungen von Hendrick Goltzius*, 2 vols., Utrecht 1961.

Rhyne 1981
C. Rhyne, 'Constable Drawings and Watercolors in the Collections of Mr. and Mrs. Paul Mellon and the Yale Center for British Art. Part I. Authentic Works', *Master Drawings*, XIX, 1981, 123–145.

Richardson 1976
F.L. Richardson, 'Some Pen Drawings by Andrea Schiavone', *Master Drawings*, XIV, 1976, 32–39.

Richardson 1980
F.L. Richardson, *Andrea Schiavone*, Oxford 1980.

Ridolfi 1648
C. Ridolfi, *Le maraviglie dell'arte*, Venice 1648.

Ridolfi/Engass 1984
C. Ridolfi, *The Life of Tintoretto*, trans. by C. Engass and R. Engass, University Park 1984.

Van Rijckevorsel 1932
J.L.A.A.M. van Rijckevorsel, *Rembrandt en de traditie*, Rotterdam 1932.

Robaut 1885
A. Robaut, *L'Oeuvre complet de Eugène Delacroix*, Paris 1885, reprinted New York 1969.

Robert-Dumesnil 1842
A.P.F. Robert-Dumesnil, *Le Peintre-graveur français*, 11 vols., Paris, 1835–71.

Roland Michel 1984
M. Roland Michel, *Watteau. Un artiste au XVIIIe siècle*, London 1984.

Rosenberg 1956, 1959
J. Rosenberg, [Review of Benesch 1954–57], *Art Bulletin*, XXXVIII, 1956, 63–70 and XLI, 1959, 108–119.

Rosenberg 1971
P. Rosenberg, [Review of M. Röthlisberger 1968], *La Revue de l'Art*, XIV, 1971, 115–116.

Rosenberg and Brejon de Lavergnée 1986
P. Rosenberg with B. Brejon de Lavergnée, *Saint-Non, Fragonard, Panopticon Italiano . . .*, Rome 1986.

Rosenblum 1967 (I)
R. Rosenblum, *Jean-Auguste-Dominique Ingres*, New York 1967.

Rosenblum 1967 (II)
R. Rosenblum, *Transformations in Late Eighteenth-Century Art*, Princeton 1967.

Rosenblum 1976
R. Rosenblum, *Cubism and Twentieth-Century Art*, 3rd ed., Englewood Cliffs and New York 1976.

Rosenthal 1977
D.A. Rosenthal, 'A Mughal Portrait copied by Delacroix', *Burlington Magazine*, CXIX, 1977, 505–506.

Rosenthal 1983
M. Rosenthal, *Constable. The Painter und his Landscape*, New Haven and London 1983.

Rossi 1975
P. Rossi, *I disegni di Jacopo Tintoretto*, Florence 1975.

Rotermund 1963
H.-M. Rotermund, *Rembrandts Handzeichnungen und Radierungen zur Bibel*, Stuttgart 1963.

Röthlisberger 1959
M. Röthlisberger, 'Les Fresques de Claude Lorrain', *Paragone*, IX, 1959, 41–50.

Röthlisberger 1961
M. Röthlisberger, *Claude Lorrain, The Paintings*, 2 vols., New Haven 1961.

Röthlisberger 1968
M. Röthlisberger, *Claude Lorrain, The Drawings*, 2 vols., Berkeley and Los Angeles 1968.

Röthlisberger 1969
M. Röthlisberger, 'Constable after Claude', *Master Drawings*, VII, 1969, 426–427.

Russoli and Minervino 1970
F. Russoli and F. Minervino, *Degas*, Milan 1970.

Sabartes 1959
J. Sabartes, *Picasso Variations on Velazquez' Painting 'The Maids of Honor' and other recent works*, New York 1959.

De Salas 1970
X. de Salas, 'Sur cinq dessins de Goya Acquis par le Musée du Prado', *Gazette des Beaux-Arts*, LXXV, 1970, 29–42.

Sandrart 1675
J. von Sandart, *Teutsche Academie*, [Nuremburg 1675] ed. by A.R. Peltzer, Munich 1925, reprinted Munich 1975.

Sandoz 1980
M. Sandoz, *Louis-Jacques Durameau 1733–1796*, Paris 1980.

Sarre 1904, 1909
F. Sarre, 'Rembrandts Zeichnungen nach indisch-islamischen miniaturen', *Jahrbuch der preussischen Kunstsammlungen*, XXV, 1904, 143–158, and idem., 1909, 283–290.

Schatborn 1985
P. Schatborn, *Catalogus van de Nederlandse Tekeningen in het Rijksprentenkabinet, Rijksmuseum, Amsterdam/Catalogue of the Dutch and Flemish Drawings in the Rijksprentenkabinet, Rijksmuseum, Amsterdam. IV. Tekeningen van/Drawings by Rembrandt, zijn onbekende leerlingen en navolgers/his anonymous pupils and followers*, The Hague 1985.

Schiff 1973
G. Schiff, *Johann Heinrich Füssli, 1741–1825*, 2 vols., Zürich 1973.

Schiff 1986
G. Schiff, 'The Sabines, Sketchbook No. 163, 1962', *Je Suis le Cahier. The Sketchbooks of Picasso*, A. Glimcher and M. Glimcher, eds., Boston and New York 1986, 179–209.

Schneider 1984
P. Schneider, *Matisse*, New York 1984.

Schoonbaert 1968
L.M.A. Schoonbaert, 'Addendum Beschrijvende Catalogus 1948. Een verzameling tekeningen van James Ensor (1e deel), *Jaarboek van het Koninklijk Museum voor Schone Kunsten Antwerpen*, 1968, 311–342.

Schoonbaert 1972
L.M.A. Schoonbaert, 'Zeichnungen', in Stuttgart 1972, 123–128.

Schulz 1971
W. Schulz, 'Doomer and Savery', *Master Drawings*, IX, 1971, 253–259.

Schulz 1974
W. Schulz, *Lambert Doomer, sämtliche Zeichnungen*, Berlin and New York 1974.

Schulz 1982
W. Schulz, *Herman Saftleven 1609–1685*, Berlin and New York 1982.

Seidlitz 1907
W. von Seidlitz, 'Dürers frühe Zeichnungen', *Jahrbuch der königlich preussischen Kunstsammlungen*, XXVIII, 1907, 3–20.

Seligman 1969
G. Seligman, *Roger de la Fresnaye, with a catalogue raisonné*, New York 1969.

Sérullaz 1963
M. Sérullaz, *Les Peintures Murales de Delacroix*, Paris 1963.

Sérullaz 1980/81
M. Sérullaz 'Delacroix und Goya', in Hamburg 1980/81, 23–27.

Sérullaz 1984
M. Sérullaz, *Inventaire général des Dessins. Ecole Française. Dessins d'Eugène Delacroix*, 2 vols., Paris 1984.

Slatkes 1965
L.J. Slatkes, *Dirck van Baburen*, Utrecht 1965.

Slatkes 1983
L.J. Slatkes, *Rembrandt and Persia*, New York 1983.

Slatkin 1976
R.S. Slatkin, 'Abraham Bloemaert and François Boucher: Affinity and Relationship', *Master Drawings*, XIV, 1976, 247–260.

Slive 1965
S. Slive, *Drawings of Rembrandt*, 2 vols., New York 1965.

Smith 1981
G. Smith, 'Tintoretto and Michelangelo's St. Damian', *Burlington Magazine* CXXVI, 1981, 614.

Springer 1906
J. Springer, 'Dürers Zeichnungen in neuen Publikationen', *Repertorium für Kunstwissenschaft* XXIX, 1906, 553–570.

Stchoukine 1929
I. Stchoukine, *La Peinture Indienne à l'Epoque des Grands Moghols*, Paris 1929.

Stechow 1942
W. Stechow, 'Rembrandt and Titian', *Art Quarterly*, V, 1942, 135–147.

Stechow 1968
W. Stechow, *Rubens and the Classical Tradition*, Cambridge 1968.

Stechow 1969
W. Stechow, 'Some Observations on Rembrandt and Lastman', *Oud Holland*, LXXXIV, nos. 2–3, 1969, 148–162.

Stechow 1971
W. Stechow, 'Rembrandt's Woman with an Arrow', *Art Bulletin*, XLI, 1971, 487–492.

Steinberg 1972
L. Steinberg, 'The Algerian Women and Picasso at Large', *Other Criteria, Confrontations with Twentieth-Century Art*, New York 1972.

Stevens 1984
M.A. Stevens, *The Orientalists: Delacroix to Matisse. The Allure of North America and the Far East*, exh. cat., Royal Academy, London and National Gallery, Washington 1984.

Strauss 1974
W. Strauss, *The Complete Drawings of Albrecht Dürer*, New York 1974.

Strauss et al. 1979
W. Strauss and M. van der Meulen-Schregardus, eds., *The Rembrandt Documents*, New York 1979.

Strong 1969
R. Strong, *National Portrait Gallery. Tudor and Jacobean Portraits*, 2 vols., London 1969.

Strzygowski 1923
J. Strzygowski, *Die Indischen Miniaturen im Schlosse Schönbrunn*, Vienna 1923.

Sutton 1980
D. Sutton, 'Jean-Honoré Fragonard: the World as Illusion', in *Fragonard*, exh. cat., Tokyo National Museum of Western Art, 1980.

Symmons 1971
S. Symmons, 'John Flaxman and Francesco Goya: Infernos Transcribed', *Burlington Magazine*, CXIII, 1971, 508–512.

Symmons 1973
S. Symmons, 'Géricault, Flaxman and Ugolino', *Burlington Magazine*, CXV, 1973, 671–672.

Symmons 1984
S. Symmons, *Flaxman and Europe. The Outline Illustrations and their Influence*, New York and London 1984.

Ternois 1980
D. Ternois, [Review of Naef 1977–80], *Master Drawings*, XVIII, 1980, 379–381.

Thausing 1884
M. Thausing, *Dürer. Geschichte seines Lebens und seiner Kunst*, 2nd ed., 2 vols., Leipzig 1884.

Thiem 1977
C. Thiem, *Florentiner Zeichner des Frühbarock*, Munich 1977.

Thuillier and Foucart 1967
J. Thuillier and J. Foucart, *Rubens' Life of Marie de' Medici*, New York 1967.

Tietze-Conrat 1927
E. Tietze-Conrat, 'Zu Dürers Zeichnung der Auferstandenen im Kupferstichkabinett', *Berliner Museen*, XLVIII, 1927, 89–92.

Tietze and Tietze-Conrat 1928–38
H. Tietze and E. Tietze-Conrat, *Kritisches Verzeichnis der Werke Albrecht Dürers*, 3 vols., Augsburg, Basel and Leipzig 1928–38.

Tietze and Tietze-Conrat 1944
H. Tietze and E. Tietze-Conrat, *The Drawings of the Venetian Painters in the 15th and 16th Centuries*, New York 1944.

Tolnay 1943
C. de Tolnay, *The Youth of Michelangelo*, Princeton 1943.

Tolnay 1954
C. de Tolnay, *The Tomb of Julius II*, Princeton 1954.

Tolnay 1975
C. de Tolnay, *Corpus dei disegni di Michelangelo*, 4 vols., Novara 1975.

Tomoroy 1972
P. Tomoroy, *The Life and Art of Henry Fuseli*, New York and Washington 1972.

Tornézy 1895
M.A. Tornézy, ed., *Bergeret et Fragonard, Journal inédit d'un voyage en Italie 1773–1774*, Paris 1895.

Trapp 1971
F. Trapp, *The Attainment of Delacroix*, Baltimore 1971.

Tümpel 1969
C. Tümpel, 'Studien zur Ikonographie der Historien Rembrandts', *Nederlands Kunsthistorisch Jaarboek*, XX, 1969, 107–198.

Tümpel 1986
C. Tümpel, *Rembrandt*, Amsterdam, 1986.

Valentiner 1923
W.R. Valentiner, 'Deutung der Judenbraut', *Kunst und Künstler*, 1923.

Valentiner 1925, 1934
W.R. Valentiner, *Rembrandt. Des Meisters Handzeichnungen*, 2 vols., Berlin, Leipzig, Stuttgart 1925, 1934.

Valentiner 1949
W.R. Valentiner, 'A Late Drawing by Leonardo', *Burlington Magazine*, XCI, 1949, 343.

Vasari/Milanesi 1568
G. Vasari, *Le Vite* [1568], ed. by G. Milanesi, Florence 1878–85.

Venturi 1927
A. Venturi, *Studi dal vero*, Milan 1927.

Venturi 1936
L. Venturi, *Cézanne, son art, son oeuvre*, Paris 1936.

Vilain 1980
J. Vilain, 'A propos de quelques dessins français de la période néo-classique', *La donation Baderou au musée de Rouen. Ecole française, Etudes de la Revue du Louvre*, I, 1980, 113–118.

Virch 1956
C. Virch, 'A Study by Tintoretto after Michelangelo', *Metropolitan Museum of Art Bulletin*, N.S. XV, 1956, 111–116.

Virch 1962
C. Virch, *Master Drawings in the Collection of Walter C. Baker*, New York 1962.

Vitali 1963
L. Vitali, 'Three Italian Friends of Degas', *Burlington Magazine*, CV, 1963, 266–273.

Voss 1953
H. Voss, 'François Boucher's early Development', *Burlington Magazine*, XCV, 1953, 82.

Van de Waal 1969
H. van de Waal, 'Light and Dark: Rembrandt and Chiaroscuro', *Delta*, XII, no. 2, 1969, 74–88.

Van de Waal 1974
H. van de Waal, *Steps Towards Rembrandt* [1956], ed. by R.H. Fuchs, transl. by P. Wardel and A. Griffiths, Amsterdam and London 1974.

Walker 1933
J. Walker, 'Degas et les maîtres anciens', *Gazette des Beaux-Arts*, X, 1933, 173–185.

Wegner 1973
W. Wegner, *Kataloge der Staatlichen Graphischen Sammlung München, Die niederländischen Handzeichnungen des 15.-18. Jahrhunderts*, 2 vols., Munich 1973.

Weinberger 1967
M. Weinberger, *Michelangelo the Sculptor*, London and New York 1967.

Weisbach 1926
W. Weisbach, *Rembrandt*, Berlin 1926.

Weixlgärtner 1903
A. Weixlgärtner, 'Dürer und die Gliederpuppe', *Beiträge zur Kunstgeschichte Franz Wickhoff gewidmet von einem Kreise von Freunden und Schülern*, Vienna 1903, 80–90.

Wethey 1975
H.E. Wethey, *The Paintings of Titian. III. The Mythological and Historical Paintings*, London 1975.

White 1962
C. White, *The Drawings of Rembrandt*, London 1962.

White 1968
C. White, *Rembrandt and His World*, New York 1968.

White 1971
C. White, *Dürer, the Artist and his Drawings*, London 1971.

Wilde 1932
J. Wilde, 'Eine Studie Michelangelos nach der Antike', *Mitteilungen des Kunsthistorischen Institutes in Florenz*, IV, July 1932, 41–64.

Wilde 1978
J. Wilde, *Michelangelo*, Oxford 1978.

Wiles 1932
K. Wiles, 'Tribolo in his Michelangelesque Vein', *Art Bulletin*, XIV, 1932, 59–70.

Williamson 1919
G.C. Williamson, 'Mr. Francis Wellesley's Collection of Miniatures and Drawings, Part III', *The Connoisseur*, LIII, April 1919.

Winkler 1936–39
F. Winkler, *Die Zeichnungen Albrecht Dürers*, 4 vols., Berlin 1936–39.

Zervos 1932–78
C. Zervos, *Pablo Picasso*, 33 vols., Paris 1932–78.

Zervos 1960
C. Zervos, 'Confrontations de Picasso avec des oeuvres d'art d'autrefois', *Cahiers d'Art*, 33e–35e années, 1960, 9–119.

Exhibitions and Catalogues

Amsterdam 1933
Rubens-Tentoonstelling, Kunsthandel J. Goudstikker, 1933.

Amsterdam 1934
Italiaansche Kunst in Nederlandsch Bezit, foreword by F. Schmidt-Degener, Stedelijk Museum, 1934.

Amsterdam 1935
Antoine Watteau als teekenaar, Willet-Holthuysen Museum, 1935.

Amsterdam 1938
Fransche Meesters uit de XIXde eeuw, Paul Cassirer, 1938.

Amsterdam 1963
Fodor 100 jaar, Tentoonstelling van een keuze uit de collectie Fodor, Museum Fodor, 1963.

Amsterdam 1969
Rembrandt 1669/1969, exh. cat. by P.J.J. van Thiel, L.C.J. Frerichs, P. Schatborn et al., Rijksmuseum, 1969.

Amsterdam 1974
Franse Tekenkunst van de 18de eeuw uit Nederlandse Verzamelingen exh. cat. by J.W. Niemeijer with P. Schatborn, Rijksmuseum, Rijksprentenkabinet, 1974.

Amsterdam 1986
Rembrandt en zijn voorbeelden/Rembrandt and his sources, exh. cat. by B. Broos, Rembrandthuis, 1986.

Antwerp 1956
Tekeningen van P.P. Rubens, exh. cat. by L. Burchard and R.-A. d'Hulst, Rubenshuis, 1956.

Baden-Baden 1974
Juan Gris, exh. cat. by D. Cooper, Kunsthalle, 1974.

Baltimore 1971
Matisse as a Draughtsman, exh. cat. by V. Carlson, Baltimore Museum of Art, 1971.

Basel 1935
Meisterzeichnungen französischer Künstler von Ingres bis Cézanne, Kunsthalle, 1935.

Basel 1943
Kunstwerke des 19. Jahrhunderts aus Basler Privatbesitz, Kunsthalle, 1943.

Basel 1948
Rembrandt-Ausstellung, Katz Galerie, 1948.

Basel 1984
Tobias Stimmer, Spätrenaissance am Oberrhein. 1539–84, Kunstmuseum, 1984.

Berkeley 1968
Master Drawings from California Collections, University Gallery, University of California, 1968.

Berlin 1930
Rembrandt-Ausstellung, Preussische Akademie der bildenden Künste, 1930.

Berlin 1967/68
Dürer und seine Zeit. Meisterzeichnungen aus dem Berliner Kupferstichkabinett, exh. cat. by H. Möhle and F. Anzelewsky, Staatliche Museen Preussischer Kulturbesitz, Kupferstichkabinett, 1967/68.

Berlin 1974
Die holländische Landschaftszeichnung 1600–1740, exh. cat. by W. Schultz, Staatliche Museen Preussischer Kulturbesitz, Kupfertichkabinett, 1974.

Bern 1963
Eugène Delacroix, exh. cat. by F. Baumann and H. Wagner, Kunstmuseum, 1963.

Besançon 1956
Exposition J.H. Fragonard, exh. cat., Musée des Beaux-Arts, Besançon, 1956.

Bielefeld 1979
Zeichnungen und Collagen des Kubismus : Picasso-Braque-Gris, exh. cat. by U. Weisner et al., Kunsthalle, 1979.

Bordeaux 1958
Paris et les ateliers provinçaux au XVIIIe siècle, Musée des Beaux-Arts, 1958.

Bordeaux 1961
De Tiepolo à Goya, Musée des Beaux-Arts, 1961.

Boston–St. Louis 1981
Printmaking in the Age of Rembrandt exh. cat. by C. Ackley, Museum of Fine Arts and St. Louis Art Museum, 1981.

Bremen 1964
Eugène Delacroix. 1798–1863, exh. cat. by C. von Heusinger, H. Bock, J. Schultze, Kunsthalle, 1964.

Brussels 1938/39
Dessins de Pierre-Paul Rubens, exh. cat. by E. Goldschmidt with intro. by L. van Puyvelde, Palais des Beaux-Arts, 1938/39.

Buffalo 1967
Painters of the Section d'Or, exh. cat. by R. West, Albright-Knox Art Gallery, 1967.

Cambridge 1955
Delacroix in New England Collections, Fogg Art Museum, 1955.

Cambridge 1961
Ingres and Degas, Fogg Art Museum 1961.

Cambridge 1965
Memorial Exhibition of the Works from the Collection of Paul J. Sachs, exh. cat. by A. Mongan with M.L. Bennett, Fogg Art Museum, 1965.

Cambridge 1985
Master Drawings from the Woodner Collection, Fogg Art Museum, 1985.

Chicago–Minneapolis–Detroit 1969/70
Rembrandt After Three Hundred Years, exh. cat. by J.R. Judson, E. Haverkamp-Begemann, A.-M. Logan, Art Institute of Chicago, Minneapolis Institute of Arts, Detroit Institute of Arts, 1969/70.

Chicago–New York 1976
Ensor, exh. cat. by J.D. Farmer, Art Institute of Chicago and The Solomon R. Guggenheim Museum, 1976.

Cincinnati 1959
The Lehman Collection, exh. cat. by G. van Groschwitz, Cincinnati Art Museum, 1959.

Cologne–Glasgow 1939
Französische Meisterzeichnungen aus der Sammlung Franz Koenigs, exh. cat. by C. Towe, Wallraf-Richartz Museum and Glasgow Art Gallery and Museum, 1939.

Copenhagen 1935
L'Art français au XVIIIe siècle, exh. cat. by J. Lejeaux, Palais du Charlottenborg, 1935.

Copenhagen 1980
Raoul Dufy, Statens Museum for Kunst, 1980.

Detroit etc. 1981/82
From a Mighty Fortress. Prints, Drawings, and Books in the Age of Luther. 1483–1546, exh. cat. by C. Andersson and C. Talbot, Detroit Institute of Arts, National Gallery of Canada, Kunstsammlungen der Veste Coburg, 1981/82.

Dresden 1970
Dialoge. Kopie, Variation und Metamorphose alter Kunst, Kupferstichkabinett der Staatlichen Kunstsammlungen, 1970.

Florence 1964
Catalogo della mostra di disegni, manoscritti e documenti, ed. by P. Barocchi, Casa Buonarroti, Biblioteca Laurenziana, 1964.

Frankfurt 1982
Jean-Antoine Watteau. Einschiffung nach Cythera, Städtische Galerie im Städelschen Kunstinstitut, 1982.

The Hague 1952
Hollandse Tekeningen rond 1600, bijeengebracht door I.K.O.N., Rijksbureau voor Kunsthistorische Documentatie, 1952.

Hamilton–New York–Amsterdam 1985/86
The Fodor Collection: Nineteenth Century French Drawings and Watercolors from Amsterdams Historisch Museum, exh. cat. by W. Loos, Picker Art Gallery, Baruch College Art Gallery and Historisch Museum, 1985/86.

Hamburg 1980/81
Goya. Das Zeitalter der Revolutionen – Kunst um 1800, exh. cat. by W. Hofmann et al., Kunsthalle, 1980/81.

Liège 1980
Raoul Dufy, Musée Saint-Georges, 1980.

Lille 1985
Au temps de Watteau, Fragonard et Chardin. Les Pays-Bas et les peintres français du XVIIIe siècle, Musée des Beaux-Arts, 1985.

London 1835
A Catalogue of One Hundred Drawings by Sir Peter Paul Rubens. Collected by Sir Thomas Lawrence, The Lawrence Gallery, 1835.

London 1928
Guide to the Woodcuts, Drawings, and Engravings of Albrecht Dürer, exh. cat. by C. Dodgson and K.T. Parker, British Museum, 1928.

London 1953
Drawings by Old Masters, Royal Academy of Arts, 1953.

London 1953/54
Flemish Art. 1300–1700, Royal Academy of Arts, 1953/54.

London–Birmingham–Leeds 1962
Old Master Drawings from the Collection of Mr. C.R. Rudolf, exh. cat. by P. Pouncey, C. White, P. Hulton, The Arts Council Gallery, City Museum and Art Gallery and City Art Gallery, 1962.

London 1964
Delacroix, exh. cat. by L. Eitner, Arts Council of Great Britain, 1964.

London 1966
Old Master Drawings. A Loan Exhibition from the National Gallery of Scotland, Colnaghi's, 1966.

London 1971 (I)
Art into Art. Works of Art as a Source of Inspiration, exh. cat. by K. Roberts, Burlington Magazine and Sotheby's, 1971.

London 1971 (II)
The Graphic Works of Albrecht Dürer: An Exhibition of Drawings and Prints in Commemoration of the Quincentenary of his Birth, British Museum, 1971.

London 1975
Henry Fuseli 1741–1825, exh. cat. G. Schiff, Tate Gallery, 1975.

London 1976
Dutch and Flemish Drawings 16th–19th Centuries, Colnaghi & Co. Ltd., 1976.

London 1977
Rubens. Drawings and Sketches, exh. cat. by J. Rowlands, British Museum, 1977.

London 1979
John Flaxman, ed. by D. Bindman, Royal Academy of Arts, 1979.

London 1981
Drawing. Technique and Purpose, exh. cat. by S. Lambert, Victoria and Albert Museum, 1981.

London 1983
The Genius of Venice. 1500–1600, exh. cat. by J. Martineau and C. Hope, Royal Academy of Arts, 1983.

London–Paris–Boston 1985
Renoir, exh. cat. by J. House, A. Distel, L. Gowing, Hayward Gallery, Grand Palais, Museum of Fine Arts, 1985.

London 1987
Master Drawings. The Woodner Collection, exh. cat. by C. Lloyd, M.A. Stevens, N. Turner et al., Royal Academy of Arts, 1987.

Los Angeles 1949
Leonardo da Vinci, County Museum, 1949.

Los Angeles 1961
Rococo to Romanticism, University of California, 1961.

Los Angeles–Detroit–Philadelphia 1971/72
Géricault, exh. cat. by L. Eitner, 1971/72.

Madrid 1986/87
Dibujos de los siglos XIV al XX. Collección Woodner, Museo del Prado, 1986/87.

Manchester–London 1975
Watercolours by Thomas Girtin, exh. cat. by F. Hawcroft, Whitworth Art Gallery and The Victoria and Albert Museum, 1975.

Milan 1977
Johann Heinrich Füssli. Disegni e Dipinti, exh. cat. by L. Vitali, Museo Poldi-Pezzoli, 1977.

Minneapolis etc. 1962
The Nineteenth Century: 125 Master Drawings, exh. cat. by L. Eitner, University Gallery, University of Minnesota and The Solomon R. Guggenheim Museum, New York, 1962.

Minneapolis 1980
Picasso from the Musée Picasso, Paris, exh. cat. by D. Bozo, M. Friedman, R. Rosenblum, R. Penrose, Walker Art Center, 1980.

Munich 1967
Italienische Zeichnungen 15.–18. Jahrhundert, exh. cat. by A. Schmitt, Staatliche Graphische Sammlung, 1967.

Munich 1983
Im Licht von Claude Lorrain. Landschaftsmalerei aus drei Jahrhunderten, exh. cat. by M. Röthlisberger et al., Haus der Kunst, 1983.

Munich 1986
Meisterzeichnungen aus Sechs Jahrhunderten. Die Sammlung Ian Woodner, Haus der Kunst, 1986.

Munster 1973
Le Dessin français du XVIe au XVIIIe siècle vu à travers les collections du Musée des Beaux Arts d'Orléans, 1973.

Munster 1976
Bilder nach Bildern, exh. cat. by G. Langemeyer and R. Schleier, 1976.

New Haven 1977
English Landscape 1630–1850 : Drawings, Prints and Books from the Paul Mellon Collection, exh. cat. by C. White, Yale Center for British Art, 1977.

New York 1918
Rembrandt, Metropolitan Museum of Art, 1918.

New York 1958/59
French Drawings from American Collections : Clouet to Matisse, exh. cat. by A. Mongan et al., Metropolitan Museum of Art, 1958/59.

New York–Cambridge 1960
Rembrandt Drawings from American Collections, exh. cat. by E. Haverkamp-Begemann and F. Stampfle, Pierpont Morgan Library and the Fogg Art Museum, 1960.

New York 1965
Drawings from New York Collections. I. The Italian Renaissance, exh. cat. by J. Bean and F. Stampfle, Metropolitan Museum of Art, 1965.

New York 1973 (I)
Cézanne, the Late Years, ed. by T. Reff, Museum of Modern Art, 1973.

New York 1973 (II)
Woodner Collection. II. Old Master Drawings, exh. cat. by F.G. Schab, Schab Gallery, 1973.

New York 1975
Drawings by Benjamin West and his son Raphael Lamar West, exh. cat. by R.S. Kraemer, Pierpont Morgan Library, 1975.

New York–Paris 1977/78
Rembrandt and his Century. Dutch Drawings of the Seventeenth Century from the Collection of Frits Lugt. exh. cat. by C. van Hasselt, Pierpont Morgan Library and Institut Néerlandais, 1977/78.

New York 1978
Art About Art, exh. cat. by J. Lipman and R. Marshall, Whitney Museum of American Art, 1978.

New York 1979 (I)
Rubens and Rembrandt in their Century, exh. cat. by F. Stampfle, Pierpont Morgan Library, 1979.

New York 1979 (II)
Seventeenth-Century Dutch and Flemish Drawings from the Robert Lehman Collections, exh. cat. by G. Szabo, Metropolitan Museum of Art, 1979.

New York 1980
Pablo Picasso. A Retrospective, ed. by W. Rubin, Museum of Modern Art, 1980.

New York 1985
Liechtenstein : The Princely Collections, exh. cat., Metropolitan Museum of Art, 1985.

New York–Detroit–Paris 1986/87
François Boucher. 1703–1770, exh. cat. by A. Laing et al., Metropolitan Museum of Art, Detroit Institute of Arts, Grand Palais, 1986/87.

Newcastle upon Tyne–London 1973
Watercolour and Pencil Drawings by Cézanne, exh. cat. by L. Gowing and R. Ratcliffe, Laing Art Gallery and Hayward Gallery, 1973.

Nuremberg 1971
Albrecht Dürer 1471–1971, Germanisches Nationalmuseum, 1971.

Orléans–Paris 1975/76
Dessins français du XVIe au XVIIIe siècle du Musée des Beaux-Arts d'Orléans, Hôtel Cabu, 1975/76.

Oslo 1976
Nederlandske Tegninger (ca. 1600–ca. 1700), exh. cat. by S. Helliesen, Nasjonalgalleriet, 1976.

Padua–Florence–Venice 1968
Disegni Olandesi del Seicento. Collezione C. Hofstede de Groot di Groninga, 1968.

Paris 1908
Exposition d'oeuvres de Rembrandt, exh. cat. by F. Courboin, J. Guibert, P.A. Lemoisne, Bibliothèque Nationale, 1908.

Paris 1935 (I)
Exposition de l'Art Italien, de Cimabue à Tiepolo, exh. cat. by Gilles de la Tourette, Petit Palais, 1935.

Paris 1935 (II)
Le dessin français dans les collections du XVIIIe siècle, Gazette des Beaux-Arts (Wildenstein), 1935.

Paris 1950
Cent-cinquante chefs d'oeuvre de l'Albertina de Vienne, Bibliothèque Nationale, 1950.

Paris 1952
Musée Boymans de Rotterdam. Dessins du XVe au XIXe siècle, exh. cat. by E. Haverkamp-Begemann, Bibliothèque Nationale, 1952.

Paris 1957
Exposition de la collection Lehman de New York, exh. cat. by C. Sterling, Musée de l'Orangerie, 1957.

Paris 1961/62
Francisco Goya y Lucientes, exh. cat. by Mme. X. Desparmet-Fitz-gerald, Musée Jacquemart-André, 1961/62.

Paris–Rotterdam–Haarlem 1962
Italiaanse tekeningen in Nederlands bezit, exh. cat. by F. Lugt et al., Institut Néerlandais, Museum Boymans-van Beuningen, Teylers Museum, 1962.

Paris 1963 (I)
Centenaire d'Eugène Delacroix, exh. cat. by M. Sérullaz, Musée du Louvre, 1963.

Paris 1963 (II)
Memorial de l'Exposition Eugène Delacroix, exh. cat. by M.
Sérullaz, Musée du Louvre, 1963.
Paris 1963 (III)
Paul Signac, Musée du Louvre, 1963.
Paris–Amsterdam 1964
*Le dessin français de Claude à Cezanne dans les collections
hollandaises*, exh. cat. by C. van Hasselt, Institut Néerlandais
and Rijksmuseum, 1964.
Paris 1965
Juan Gris. Dessins et Gouaches 1910–1927, Galerie Louise
Leiris, 1965.
Paris 1967
Le Cabinet d'un Grand Amateur P.-J. Mariette 1694–1774, exh.
cat. by M. Sérullaz, R. Bacou et al., Musée du Louvre,
1967.
Paris 1967/68
Ingres, exh. cat. by M. Sérullaz et al., Petit Palais, 1967/68.
Paris 1969
Hubert Robert. Les Sanguines du Musée de Valence, Musée
Jacquemart-André, 1969.
Paris 1972
Dufy, aquarelles et dessins, Galerie Dina Vierny, 1972.
Paris 1973
Autour du Néoclassicisme, peintures, dessins, sculptures, Galerie
Cailleux, 1973.
Paris 1974
Dessins des Ecoles du Nord, Galerie Claude Aubry, 1974.
Paris 1974/75
Le Néo-Classicisme français. Dessins des Musées de Province, exh.
cat. by M. Sérullaz et al., Grand Palais, 1974/75.
Paris–Detroit–New York 1975
French Painting 1774–1830: The Age of Revolution, exh. cat. by
F.J. Cummings, P. Rosenberg, R. Rosenblum et al., Grand
Palais, Detroit Institute of Arts, Metropolitan Museum of
Art, 1975.
Paris 1976
Raoul Dufy, collections de la ville de Paris, Musée d'Art
Moderne de la Ville de Paris, 1976.
Paris 1978
Sanguines : dessins français du dix-huitième siècle, Galerie
Cailleux, 1978.
Paris 1981/82
Turner en France, exh. cat. by J. and M. Guillaud et al.,
Centre Culturel du Marais, 1981/82.
Paris 1983
Bonjour Monsieur Manet, Centre Georges Pompidou, Musée
National d'Art Moderne, Galeries Contemporaines, 1983.
Paris–New York 1983
Manet, exh. cat. by F. Cachin, C.S. Moffett, with M. Melot,
Grand Palais and Metropolitan Museum of Art, 1983.
Paris 1983/84
Hommage à Raphael. Raphael et l'art français, exh. cat. by J.
Thuillier, M. Vasselin, J.P. Cuzin et al., Grand Palais,
1983/84.
Paris 1986
*Miniatures Indiennes et Persanes de la Fondation Custodia
(Collection Frits Lugt)*, exh. cat. by C. van Hasselt, Institut
Néerlandais, 1986.

Pittsburgh etc. 1986/87
French Drawings from the Musée des Beaux-Arts d'Orleans,
Pittsburgh, Memphis, St. Petersburgh, Salt Lake City,
1986/87.
Princeton 1974
Copies as Originals. Translations in Media and Techniques, exh.
cat. by R. Goffen, D. Steadman et al., The Art Museum,
Princeton University, 1974.
Providence 1975
Rubenism, exh. cat. by M.C. Volk et al., Rhode Island
School of Design, Department of Art, Brown University
and Museum of Art, 1975.
Raleigh 1959
W.R. Valentiner, Memorial Exhibition, Masterpieces of Art,
North Carolina Museum of Art, 1959.
Rennes 1985
Jean-Germain Drouais, 1763–1788, exh. cat. by A. Sérullaz
and R. Michel, Musée des Beaux-Arts de Rennes, 1985.
Rome 1984/85
Degas e l'Italia, exh. cat. by H. Loyrette, Academy of
France, Villa Medici, 1984/85.
Rotterdam 1933/34
Teekeningen van Ingres tot Seurat, Museum Boymans, 1933/34.
Rotterdam 1934/35
Honderd oude Fransche teekeningen uit de Verzameling F. Koenigs,
Museum Boymans, 1934/35.
Rotterdam 1938
Meesterwerken uit vier eeuwen. 1400–1800, Museum Boymans,
1938.
Rotterdam 1939
Catalogus van Teekeningen van P.P. Rubens, Museum Boymans,
1939.
Rotterdam 1952
*Choix de Dessins, Exposition organisée à l'occasion du XVIIe
Congrés International d'Histoire de l'Art*, Museum Boymans,
1952.
Rotterdam–Amsterdam 1956
Rembrandt, exh. cat. by E. Haverkamp-Begemann, Museum
Boymans and Rijksmuseum, 1956.
Rotterdam–Haarlem 1958
Hendrick Goltzius als tekenaar exh. cat. by E. Haverkamp
Begemann, Museum Boymans and Teylers Museum, 1958.
St. Louis–Philadelphia–Minneapolis 1967
Drawings by Degas, exh. cat. by J.S. Boggs, City Art Museum
of St. Louis, Philadelphia Museum of Art, The Minneapolis
Society of Fine Arts, 1967.
Siegen 1927
Rubens Gedächtnis Ausstellung, Museum des Siegerlandes,
1927.
Stuttgart 1972
Ensor – ein Maler aus dem späten 19. Jahrhundert, exh. cat. by
U.M. Schneede et al., Württembergischer Kunstverein,
1972.
Tokyo 1983
Henry Fuseli, The National Museum of Western Art, 1983.
Toronto 1951
Rembrandt, Art Gallery of Toronto, 1951.
Troyes–Nîmes–Rome 1977
Charles-Joseph Natoire. 1700–1777, Musée des Beaux-Arts,
Troyes, Musée des Beaux-Arts, Nîmes, Villa Medici, 1977.

Tübingen 1978
Cézanne : das zeichnerische Werk, Kunsthalle, 1978.

Tübingen–Zürich 1982
Cézanne Watercolours, exh. cat. by G. Adriani, Kunsthalle and Kunsthaus, 1982.

Tübingen–Berlin 1984
Edgar Degas. Pastelle, Ölskizzen, Zeichnungen, exh. cat. by G. Adriani, Kunsthalle and Nationalgalerie, 1984.

Tübingen–Brussels 1986
Ingres und Delacroix. Aquarelle und Zeichnungen, exh. cat. by E. Goldschmidt and G. Adriani, Kunsthalle and Palais des Beaux-Arts, 1986.

Venice 1973
G.B. Cavalcaselle. Disegni da antichi maestri, exh. cat. by L. Moretti, Biblioteca Marciana, 1973.

Vienna 1977
Die Rubenszeichnungen der Albertina, exh. cat. by E. Mitsch, graphische Sammlung Albertina, 1977.

Vienna 1980
Original-Kopie-Replik-Paraphrase, exh. cat. by H. Hutter, Akademie der bildenden Künst, 1980.

Vienna 1986
Die Sammlung Ian Woodner, Graphische Sammlung Albertina, 1986.

Washington etc. 1958/59
Dutch Drawings. Masterpieces of Five Centuries, exh. cat. by I.Q. van Regteren Altena, National Gallery of Art etc., 1958/59.

Washington–Chicago–Boston 1971
Cézanne, an exhibition in honor of the fiftieth anniversary of the Phillips Collection, Intro. by J. Rewald, Phillips Memorial Art Gallery, Art Institute of Chicago, Boston Museum of Fine Arts, 1971.

Washington 1973
Early Italian Engravings from the National Gallery of Art, exh. cat. by J.A. Levinson, K. Oberhuber, J.L. Sheehan, National Gallery of Art, 1973.

Washington 1977
Seventeenth-Century Dutch Drawings from American Collections, exh. cat. by F.W. Robinson, National Gallery of Art, 1977.

Washington 1978 (I)
Drawings by Fragonard in North American Collections, exh. cat. by E. Williams, National Gallery of Art, 1978.

Washington 1978 (II)
Hubert Robert Drawings and Watercolors, National Gallery of Art, 1978.

Washington 1978 (III)
Master Drawings from the Collections of the National Gallery of Art and Promised Gifts, exh. cat. by A. Robison, National Gallery of Art, 1978.

Washington 1981/82
French Master Drawings from the Rouen Museum from Caron to Delacroix, exh. cat. by P. Rosenberg and F. Bergot, International Exhibitions Foundation, 1981/82.

Washington 1983
Raphael and America, exh. cat. by D.A. Brown, National Gallery of Art, 1983.

Washington 1983/84
Leonardo's Last Supper : Precedents and Reflections, exh. cat. by D.A. Brown, National Gallery of Art, 1983/84.

Washington–Parma 1984
Correggio and His Legacy. Sixteenth Century Emilian Drawings, exh. cat. by D. DeGrazia, National Gallery of Art and Galleria Nazionale di Parma, 1984.

Washington–Paris–Berlin 1984/85
Watteau 1684–1721, exh. cat. by M. Morgan Grasselli and P. Rosenberg, National Gallery of Art, Grand Palais, Schloss Charlottenburg, 1984/85.

Washington–New York 1986/87
The Age of Bruegel : Netherlandish Drawings in the Sixteenth Century, exh. cat. by J.O. Hand, J.R. Judson, W.W. Robinson and M. Wolff, National Gallery of Art and The Pierpont Morgan Library, 1986/87.

Williamstown 1960
Dutch and Flemish Masters (Exhibit Twelve), Sterling and Francine Clark Art Institute, 1960.

Zürich 1926
Johann Heinrich Füssli-Henry Fuseli (1741–1825), Kunsthaus, 1926.

Zürich 1941
Johann Heinrich Füssli, Kunsthaus, 1941.

Photographic Acknowledgements

Individual numbers refer to drawings exhibited; hyphenated numbers to figures in the text. Numbers of negatives are given in parentheses.

Copyright reserved by Her Majesty Queen Elizabeth II, Windsor Castle: 51–1.

Copright A.C.L. Brussels: 29–1, 37, 57–1.
Copyright ARS N.Y./SPADEM 1987: 71.
Fonds Albertina: 2–2, 3, 36–1.
Alinari/Art Resource, N.Y.: 1–1 (8126), 8–1 (3497), 9–1 (27962), 21–1 (7552), 28–1 (7905), 47–1 (7835), 61–1, 65–1 (22342).
Jörg P. Anders: 5, 24–1, 30, 30–1, 30–2, 31–1, 36, 39–1, 56–1.
Bob Jones University Collection, Greenville, S.C.: 46–1.
Courtesy of the Trustees of the British Museum: 4, 18–1, 21, 29, 32–2.
Photographie Bulloz: 42.
Robert Forbes: 50.
Frequin-Photos: 13–2, 17, 39, 57, 64.
Giraudon/Art Resource, N.Y.: 69–1 (LA 20067), 70–1 (190021 L).
H. Humm: 51.
B.P. Keiser: 25, 26–1.
Ralph Kleinhempel: 5–1, 5–2.
J. Lathion: 32.
Marburg/Art Resource, N.Y.: 2–1 (2880), 11–1 (2880), 31–2 (230821).
Musées de la Ville de Paris copyright by SPADEM 1987: 70.
Musées Nationaux – Paris: 1–2, 33–3, 35–3, 39–2, 40–1, 47–2, 50–1, 54–1, 68–2.
Musée des Beaux-Arts de Rennes: 49–2.
Courtesy of the Museum of Fine Arts, Boston: 20–1.
Courtesy of the Trustees of the National Gallery, London: 25–1.
Copyright The Pierpont Morgan Library, New York: 33, 47.
Copyright Rijksmuseum-Stichting, Amsterdam: 3–1, 6–1, 14–1, 15–1, 17–2, 17–3, 23–1, 25–2, 35–2, 46, 53–1, 59–1, 60–1, 60–2.
Walter Rosenblum: 28.
Scala/Art Resource, N.Y.: 7–1 (28869) 18–2 (2258), 27–1 (7197), 38–1 (23377), 48–1 (6591), 49–1 (1867), 63–1 (23363), 67–1 (22861).
Tom Scott: 22–1, 22–2.
John Stoel: 24.
Joseph Szaszfai: 26.
Universitätsbibliothek, Basel: 16–2, 16–3, 16–4, 16–5.
Walter Wachter: 43–1.

The following illustrations are from publications:

Ananoff and Wildenstein 1976: 45–1.
Bartsch 1803–21: 3–3, 20–2, 35–1.
Benesch 1957: 33–1, 33–2, 34–1.
Bindman 1978: 48–2.
Glück 1931: 44–1.
Glück and Haberditzl, 1928: 40–1.
Herbert 1962: 49–3.
Sérullaz 1984: 33–3.
Slatkin 1976: 42–1, 42–2.
Tolnay 1943: 10–1.

Illustrations not credited above were provided by the lenders.

List of Lenders

Numbers refer to catalogue entries

Her Majesty Queen Elizabeth II, Windsor Castle, Royal Library, Windsor 8

Amsterdam, Amsterdams Historisch Museum 2
Amsterdam, Rijksmuseum, Rijksprentenkabinet 7, 46
Berlin, Staatliche Museen Preussischer Kulturbesitz 5, 30, 36
Braunschweig, Herzog Anton Ulrich-Museum 25
Brussels, Musées Royaux des Beaux-Arts de Belgique 14, 37
Cambridge, Harvard University Art Museums (Fogg Art Museum) 58, 60
Chicago, The Art Institute of Chicago 66
Cleveland, The Cleveland Museum of Art 34, 43
Detroit, The Detroit Institute of Arts 65
Düsseldorf, Kunstmuseum Düsseldorf 27
Edinburgh, National Gallery of Scotland 18
Florence, Gabinetto dei Disegni e Stampe degli Uffizi 23
Groningen, Groninger Museum 24
Haarlem, Teylers Museum 11, 12
London, Trustees of the British Museum 4, 21, 29
London, The Board of the Trustees of the Victoria and Albert Museum 53
Madrid, Biblioteca Nacional 52
Malibu, The J. Paul Getty Museum 22
Mannheim, Stadtische Kunsthalle 68
Munich, Staatliche Graphische Sammlung 1
New Haven, Yale Center for British Art, Paul Mellon Collection 54
New Haven, Yale University Art Gallery 6, 26
New York, The Metropolitan Museum of Art 9, 10, 41
New York, The Metropolitan Museum of Art, Robert Lehman Collection 31
New York, The Pierpont Morgan Library 33, 47
Orléans, Musée des Beaux-Arts d'Orléans 42
Oslo, Nasjonalgalleriet 32
Paris, Musée d'Art Moderne de la Ville de Paris 70
Paris, Musée Picasso 71
Rotterdam, Museum Boymans-van Beuningen 17, 39, 57, 64
Rouen, Musée des Beaux-Arts 49
Stanford, Stanford University Museum of Art 55
Stockholm, Nationalmuseum 16
Valence, Le Musée de Valence 45
Venice, Biblioteca Nazionale Marciana 62
Veste Coburg, Kunstsammlungen der Veste Coburg 13
Vienna, Graphische Sammlung Albertina 3
Washington, National Gallery of Art 19
Williamstown, Sterling and Francine Clark Art Institute 20
Zürich, Kunsthaus 48, 51

Marianne Feilchenfeldt, Zürich 63
The Forbes Magazine Collection, New York 50
Walter Klein, New York 69
Mrs Rush Kress, New York 44
Jill Newhouse and Eric Carlson, New York 59
William E. O'Reilly, New York 67
I. Q. van Regteren Altena Heirs, Amsterdam 15
The Ian Woodner Family Collection, Inc., New York 28

Other private collections 35, 38, 40, 56, 61

Index